"Son of God"

Pat Robson

Intercelt
intercelt@aol.com

ISBN 978-0-9557727-1-9

Reprinted 2012 and 2014

Printed by:
Booths Print
The Praze
Penryn
01326 373628

ABOUT THE AUTHOR

Pat Robson was Head of Religious Education
at the Humphry Davy Boy's Grammar School in
Penzance before training for the priesthood. She has led
many study tours to the Holy Land and, after working
as a Parish Priest in the Diocese of Truro, she is now
retired and living in Cornwall.

Her other books include The Celtic Heart (Harper
Collins and SPCK), A Celtic Liturgy (Harper Collins
and SPCK) and Celtic Praise (Tim Tiley Publications).

For my grandchildren

CHAPTER ONE

He came out of the desert.

His clothing whipped against his spare form and billowed erratically as he strode forward in the fierce late afternoon wind.

Peering from the shadow of the rocks three men watched intently. The eldest, John, a gaunt weather-beaten man, stood up and craned his neck to try and see above the shimmering heat that swam over the ground.

He shaded his eyes and squinted into the distance.

No one spoke.

The figure moved steadily towards them.

At last, with a sigh of relief, John grunted 'That's him!' Turning to the others he said 'Now it's up to you!' The two younger men looked at each other with excitement, their hearts in their mouth. Quickly they gathered up their cloaks and bags and scrambled to their feet.

The man came closer.

His skin had been burnt almost black by the sun and his hair blew about his face. He moved steadily, purposefully. It wasn't until he was within yards of the three men that they could see his eyes; coal black and glittering with a fierce intensity.

Fixed on a point somewhere ahead, he strode on, not noticing the men as they moved forward to greet him. The youngest man, another John, reached out to catch his arm as he passed, but the older John pulled him back. 'Not so fast lad' he said 'He's been out in the desert a long time. He'll need time to adjust.'

'But I know him!' exclaimed the young John 'He's a cousin!'

'I know him too' said his friend with a puzzled frown 'How could it be him?'

'It's him alright' the older man said with a sense of finality 'Go on! Keep him in your sight. He's going to need friends around him when he gets the desert out of his soul.'

He gave them both a shove.

'Hurry up now. Look at how quickly he's walking. You will find it hard to keep up!'

Stumbling at first over the rough surface the young men scrambled awkwardly after the man. They glanced behind still bewildered, needing reassurance, but the older John had already turned away.

Turning back they quickened their steps. The man they were to follow was striding on, not looking right nor left. The wind whipped up the dust around him.

The young men half ran, half stumbled in their effort to keep up.

He was walking like a man possessed. What was driving him? What had he seen in the desert to press him so? Usually talkative, even John was stunned into silence, and they followed, it seemed, for hours.

With the desert behind them the road skirted around a busy town and turned north along the valley. Daylight was starting to fade. Still he strode on.

Then suddenly, without warning, he faltered, reached out a hand to steady himself, hesitated and went forward again, slower this time.

John ran forward gasping for breath

'Jesus! Stop for a moment! It's me John!' He reached out and caught the man's sleeve 'For goodness sake stop!'

The man turned. A puzzled frown appeared across his face. Pushing back his hair he looked at the two young men as though awakening from a dream.

'John! Andrew! What are you doing here?' he exclaimed.

'We were searching for you' retorted John 'At least we didn't know it was you.' He wiped sweat from his face 'It's all very confusing!'

The man looked bewildered 'What are you talking about?' he said.

Andrew pushed forward.

'Jesus' he spoke urgently 'I don't think you realise how late it's getting. Look it's almost dark and it's dangerous to be on the road. We've left Jericho behind. You've been walking for hours. We couldn't stop you. But now' he said looking around at the barren land and the empty road 'we need somewhere to stay. Shall we go back and find an inn?'

The man was silent for a moment. He looked around to get his bearings. As he did so the tension visibly left his body and his eyes became calmer.

'You're right Andrew' he said slowly 'but there's no sense in turning back. We can go on. There's an inn alongside the synagogue in the next village.'

He looked at them both. A smile creased his face. 'If you can keep up, that is!'

He reached out and took John's bag. Swinging it on his shoulder he turned to the younger man 'Put on your cloak John,' he said 'It's getting cold and you're shivering already.'

Confused by the sudden change in Jesus, John did as he was told and wrapped his cloak around his shoulders while the other two began to walk. Fastening the clasp he ran to catch them up.

They walked, one on either side of the man they had been searching for. Reaching out Jesus placed his arms lightly across each man's shoulders. 'I'm glad you found me,' he said steadily. 'I'm in great need of friends right now!'

Later, their meal finished, they reclined around a small brazier. The tongues of flame flickered and made shadows on the walls of their rented room.

'The Baptist told us that you were the Messiah' John couldn't keep it to himself any longer 'He said God spoke when you were baptised' he paused and looked at Jesus accusingly.

'It can't be true, can it? You're my cousin. You come from Galilee; you're just an ordinary person. How can it be true?'

'Something did indeed happen when I went to John for baptism' said Jesus with a solemn face. He put his mug of wine on the floor next to him and gazed for while into the flames.

When he went on his dark eyes were shot through with the flickering light.

'It feels strange to say this' he said intently 'but as I came out of the water I felt as though I was entirely alone in the world. It was a uniquely special moment.' His eyes came alive with the memory and he paused for a while

'There was just me and God and a voice in my heart telling me that I was His son and that he was pleased with me. I felt as if the very essence of God himself flowed into my body, into my very soul. My heart was beating so fast I thought it would burst. I felt scared and excited at the same time. I wanted the moment to last for ever.'

'Is that why you went into the desert, away from the crowds?' asked Andrew empathising.

'I must have behaved badly.' Jesus gave a rueful smile 'I never said a word to John. I just needed to get away on my own to make the moment last and to think.'

'What happened out there?' Andrew was cautious. 'When you came back you looked as though you had met the devil himself!'

Jesus nodded. 'I did in a way' he agreed. 'It's easy to be tempted to take the easy path.' He paused again and looked down at his hands.

'I've worked as a carpenter and builder all my life' he said and both John and Andrew nodded 'but I've always known' he continued 'that the time would come when things would change. What happened at my baptism made me realise that the time is now. John was right when he told you that I was the Messiah.'

'What!' exclaimed John in alarm. 'You're going along with all this?'

'Yes John I am' said Jesus 'I seriously am.'

'But we've had Messiah's before and they've all come to nothing' said John plaintively 'Surely you don't want to end up like one of them.'

'No, that's very true!' agreed Jesus relaxing back again on the cushions 'I used to talk about this with your brother James and with Simon, your brother Andrew. We would sit outside the inn in Capernaum when we were younger and we'd put the world to rights!'

He smiled at the memory. 'In our ideal world the Romans would be sent packing, the people would have enough food to eat and Jerusalem would be the capital of the world.'

'When the Messiah comes that's exactly what will happen' said Andrew eagerly 'that's what the prophets tell us!'

'Do they Andrew? Are you sure?'

Andrew looked confused 'Well no!' he admitted 'I didn't do much schooling. I can read and I can write but there's no call for a scholar on a fishing boat!'

Jesus laughed. 'I suppose not' he conceded 'but it's a skilful job so don't do yourself down.'

He paused for while and looked deep into the burning embers of the fire. 'The prophets talked about a time when the hearts of all men would seek after God. They didn't talk of riches and conquest. That's been the wishful thinking of an occupied suffering people.'

John's brow was furrowed as he struggled to take in what Jesus was implying. 'If you are the Messiah then, what kind of Messiah are you going to be?' he asked.

'That's what I had to decide!' replied Jesus 'That's why I went into the desert!'

'You haven't told us what happened yet' demanded Andrew.

Jesus laughed at his eagerness, but then, as he recalled those days alone in the desert his face grew serious. 'It was because of the power' he said solemnly. 'I felt the power of God inside me and I knew, I just knew without a shadow of doubt that I could make all those childish dreams come true. I could be the kind of Messiah everyone expected. With God's power how could I fail?'

Andrew leaned forward eagerly 'Well?' he urged.

Jesus paused again and looked directly into Andrew's eyes. 'What makes men seek after God, Andrew? Is it riches or conquest?'

Andrew didn't reply. He frowned in confusion. 'If people have everything they want they have no need of God' interrupted John 'Why would they bother?'

'That's exactly it!' said Jesus with a smile 'If the Messiah is to truly fulfil the prophecies he must lead people to God. It is love that leads to true contentment. The people need to know how precious they each are to God. Then they will want to seek him because their hearts will long for him.'

John and Andrew looked at each other. John raised his eyebrows and made a comical grimace. 'So you won't be getting rid of the Romans' he said bluntly.

'You're so right!' said Jesus with a laugh 'I'm certainly not going to be the kind of Messiah the people expect.'

'They'll find it very hard to take' said Andrew with a frown 'and it won't be easy for you either.'

'I know Andrew' said Jesus sadly. 'I'm sorry if I've disappointed you both but you need to know before you agree to stay with me just what you are signing up to.'

'Stay with you?' said John eagerly. 'Do you want us?'

'If you can face being friends with a non-Messiah I would feel privileged to have your company.'

'What about this power or energy that you've got?' asked Andrew anxiously 'It was driving you when you came out of the desert. It had taken you over completely. It was frightening. Are you able to control it?'

'I don't know Andrew!' answered Jesus honestly 'All I know is that my father wants me to do his work and has given me his power to help me. The way I use this power is important. It is the power that created and fashioned the world. Nothing can stand in its way. It is love itself and it flows directly from the heart of God. It can never be used for evil or selfish ends. I learnt that much at least while I was in the desert.'

He looked down into the eyes of the two men.

'The way ahead will be hard. I could do with some friends.'

Andrew looked up and caught his gaze 'Count me in' he said quietly.

'And me!' said John jumping to his feet with excitement. He looked at Jesus 'I don't know why but I never thought of you as a rebel before. Now I think it may be possible that you could turn the whole world on its head and I can't wait for us to start!'

CHAPTER TWO

They left well before dawn the next day and had walked several miles before the sun rose over the east cliff of the valley.

By midday they were glad to rest for a while under a lone sycamore tree. It was too hot to talk but they drank the water from their old wine skins and ate some bread and figs.

It felt good to stop and they sat lost in their own thoughts until the sun tipped over its zenith.

Then Jesus spoke 'I would like to stay here for a while' he said 'If you two go on ahead you could get as far as Beth Shan by night fall.'

'You still want us with you though, don't you? You're not trying to get rid of us?' Alarm flickered in John's eyes.

Jesus looked at him and laughed 'Of course I want you with me John. It's your enthusiasm that will keep me going and your continual questions that will keep my feet on the ground. You are very important to me! But to be serious' he continued 'if you leave now you could be in Capernaum by this time tomorrow.'

'We should be able to' agreed Andrew. 'Is there something you want us to do?'

'I'd like you both to find your brothers. Find James and Simon and give them this message from me. Just say that I said "The time has come!" They will know what you mean!'

'Are you sure?' asked John incredulously. 'Just "the time has come"?'

'Yes, they will know' replied Jesus. 'And if you find Philip or Thomas give them the same message. Tell them that I will see them at your mother's house tomorrow evening. I will get there by then. It will be good to meet your parents and sisters again.'

'Will you be alright on your own?' Andrew looked anxious.

Jesus smiled 'But I'm not alone Andrew and that is why I need to stay. I have things to talk over and like John I have many questions to ask. I'll be quite safe and I'll get to Bethsaida by tomorrow evening' he reassured them.

Andrew and John scrambled to their feet and Jesus stepped forward and took them by the hand. 'Don't look so worried. I have been alone before and I'm sure I will be again.'

He watched as they walked away down the road and then with a light step and a sense of happy anticipation he took his shawl from around his neck, covered his head and turned aside to face the barren cliffs to be alone with God.

True to his word he arrived at John's family house in Bethsaida just as the lamps were being lit. John and Andrews' faces showed their pride as they ushered him in to the living room. John's mother came forward and he kissed her cheeks 'It's so good to see you again my favourite aunt' teased Jesus. 'I'm sorry that I'm using your house like this without asking you first. Please forgive me!'

'I love to see all you young people' replied Salome 'you are always welcome. Zebedee will be here soon but he's getting on now. Don't expect him to know who you are!'

'I remember aunt. Don't worry! Is he well in himself?'

'Strong as an ox and still fishing with the boys' his aunt replied 'just very forgetful! And that reminds me, have you been to see your mother yet?'

'I'm spending the Sabbath in Capernaum then I will be going to Nazareth. I'll be seeing her very soon so don't worry!' Jesus smiled his reply and looked around the room. 'James! Philip! Oh how good it is to see you after all this time. You got my message then. Thank you for coming!'

He embraced each man 'It's been so long!' he said. 'Where are Simon and Thomas? Couldn't they come?'

John pushed forward. 'Thomas is in Nazareth. He's still busy on a project in Sepphoris. We just haven't had time to get there and find him.'

'Never mind' said Jesus 'We're going there next week, we'll find him ourselves. And Simon?'

Andrew flushed. 'He wouldn't come. I gave him your message and he said "What? That old dream? I'm an old man now, I've got responsibilities" and he flatly refused to come.

Jesus laughed 'Old man indeed! He's thirty if he's a day, the same as me. I expect he's gone fishing!'

Andrew smiled ruefully 'Well yes!' he said 'he'll be out all night.'

'And he'll be like a bear with a sore head in the morning' said Jesus still chuckling. 'Don't worry Andrew, I'll find him tomorrow. He's a law unto himself, always has been, but God has plans for him!' He looked around 'He has plans for you all. Why don't I tell you what's going on?' he said lowering himself until he was sitting cross-legged on the floor. The four men joined him eagerly. The women discreetly left the room and the young men were left alone.

After a moment of silence Jesus began to talk. As the evening wore on the women came back with bowls of steaming broth and bread and by the time the moon had risen high in the sky and the lights had all gone out in the little town the lives of four young men had changed forever.

The next morning, while the others slept, Jesus kissed his aunt and slipped out of the house. He took the path down to the lake and then walked along the small beach towards Capernaum.

The rising sun was already hot and the water shimmered and sparkled in the light breeze. Jesus took his cloak from his shoulders and dressed only in his long white shift he revelled in feeling the sun on his back and listening to the birds as they flitted in and out of the gently swaying reeds. It was a glorious day.

Capernaum, when he reached it, was beginning to wake. A few men had gathered by the quay side and a woman was setting up a stall selling hot food on the road side. The smell of hot bread reached him and Jesus left the shore and walked over to her and bought a piece of grilled fish and some hot crusty bread. A thin dog nudged his leg and he smiled down at it 'Come on friend. Come and share this with me!' and he sat down on a low wall and broke off a piece of the bread. 'Enjoy!' he said giving it to the hungry animal. They sat for a moment in companionable silence.

Moments later returning to the shore, Jesus scanned the lake for Simon's boat. It was not yet alongside the harbour wall so Simon and his crew must still be out there somewhere.

He walked further on to the point of the small headland and there in a pool of sunlight was Simon's boat bobbing gently in the next bay. There was only one man aboard.

He walked down to the beach. 'Simon!' he called. The man on the boat did not move. 'Simon' this time a little louder.

The man straightened up and looked at Jesus.

'Have you had a good night's fishing?' called Jesus.

'No!' grunted the man turning away.

Jesus laughed 'You're always so bad tempered after you've been awake all night. You're getting too old for this. Fishing is a young man's job!'

'Old!' roared the man 'I'm not old. I'm in my prime!'

'Yes I know you are' conceded Jesus. 'Have you tried putting your nets out on the other side?'

'Are you telling me how to fish now?' Simon roared again, his face becoming red with indignation.

'Just try!' urged Jesus.

'I've been out all night. My nets have been out first this side and then the other. There are just no fish to be caught!'

'Go on Simon, humour me!' Jesus smiled in the face of his friend.

'It'll be a waste of time' grunted Simon but he gathered his net over his arm and crossed to the other side of the boat. For a moment he hesitated, silhouetted against the white horizon. Then with a skilled movement he twisted his right arm and the net spun out into a circle above his head and dropped into the water without even a splash.

Simon turned and looked at Jesus 'There!' he said 'Satisfied?'

'Pull it in Simon! Don't be afraid!' he teased.

Simon stood tall 'I know what's going to happen' he said 'I'm not afraid and you know it! It's going to be full of fish isn't it?'

'Pull it in!' urged Jesus again.

With a resigned shrug Simon bent to grasp the net. It took all of his strength and as the mouth of the net reached the gunwales it opened and silver fish flapped and slithered into the hull.

Simon looked down in resigned bewilderment.

'How did you do that?' he demanded 'Could you see the shoal from the beach?'

'Pull the boat in a bit closer' called Jesus ''I'll come on board and help you.'

Simon reached for a pole and pushed it down into the water. Leaning on it and pushing with all his strength the boat moved towards the shore.

Jesus threw his cloak and sandals on to the prow and waded out to grab the gunwale and heaved himself into the boat.

He greeted Simon with a slap on the shoulder. 'You really are a grumpy old sod!' he said with a grin.

'I didn't come to your meeting last night' replied Peter with a belligerent shrug.

'I know you didn't' replied Jesus 'so I thought I'd come to you instead.'

'Is it really now?' Simon asked with an anxious frown. 'It's ages since we were kids and talked about this moment. I thought that perhaps it was all a dream. I'm married now and I have children. I really don't think I can be part of it all.' He slumped down in the boat.

'I know what that's like' Jesus agreed. 'When my father died I had so many responsibilities. As the eldest I had to take on my father's role. Luckily he had taught me a trade and Antipas needed builders at Sepphoris so I've had steady employment. I too thought the time would never come.' He paused 'Do you remember how we used to meet up outside the inn in Capernaum, you and me, James Philip and Thomas? It didn't take long for us to solve the problems of the world over a mug of wine, did it?'

'It all seemed so easy then' agreed Simon ruefully. 'But now it's impossible!'

'Harder yes!' said Jesus 'but not impossible. He paused 'It's easier for me. My brothers are all settled. James is at rabbinic school in Jerusalem and the other three are contracted to work on the Sepphoris site. Joanna is married and little Dorcas is still at home with mother.'

'My boys are only six and eight' said Peter 'You know I live in Capernaum now don't you? My wife's family are fairly well off and it's a better place from which to run a business. I still love Bethsaida but it's a dozy little place compared to Capernaum. My business is doing well' he said with pride. 'I employ six men you know!'

'You're on your own this morning' Jesus commented gently.

Simon looked embarrassed 'It's the wrong time of the year for fishing. We laid the men off for a few weeks. I only came out in the boat to avoid you!' He laughed 'I should have guessed you'd find me anyway!'

Jesus laughed with him. Looking directly into his friend's honest wide eyes he said 'Look Simon, I know it's not an easy time for you. Can I come to your house tonight and stay the entire Sabbath? I will need to go on up to Nazareth the following day but we will have more time to talk and you'll have more time to think.'

'Sounds good to me old friend' said Simon with relief 'Of course you can stay.' He looked down at the fish 'Now you can help me with this lot. After all it must have been something you did or said that made them happen. I cannot believe it was just a coincidence.' He paused 'Perhaps I should employ you, I'd make a fortune.'

'You really are an idiot' laughed Jesus 'Get down these baskets and I'll begin sorting. If you put up the sail we can get back to Capernaum before Tabitha has sold out of all her fresh bread!'

'You're on' said Simon with a grin. 'Are you buying?'

'I suppose I am' replied Jesus happily.

CHAPTER THREE

Despite her small stature nobody in their right mind would even dream of upsetting Irena. Simon's mother-in-law was a tiny, bustling person with a big laugh and a fiery temper. 'It's no good inviting you back to the house just now' Simon said with a mouthful of hot bread 'Irena and my Sarah will be working all day to make it spotless for the Sabbath tonight. They'll be beating carpets, sweeping, polishing, cooking; in fact they'll be doing every possible kind of housework activity they can think of. We'd have short shrift from them if we even tried to put a foot inside!'

'There must be jobs you need to do around the boat' replied Jesus giving the last of his bread to the dog and standing up and brushing the crumbs from his clothes.

'Well yes' said Simon 'There are two nets that need repairing and if you're going to hang around perhaps you could try and mend that seat in the stern. There are tools in a box in the boat.'

'It sounds as if it could be a perfect day' replied Jesus 'Just as it was when we were kids and my parents dragged us down from Nazareth to the market. That was such a long walk for young children but it was a real treat all the same. We could swim and fish and play while they went to market and met up with relatives. Looking back those were idyllic days.'

The two men walked back to the boat.

'It's strange isn't it' mused Simon 'That, whatever we do in life and no matter how much time passes, when you have childhood friends and you meet up again you just seem to pick up where you left off. I meet so many people in my business but there's nothing to compare with old friendships.'

'That's why I'm here Simon' Jesus' face was grave and earnest.

'I came here to ask my old childhood friends, men I know through and through, men I can trust, to join me and help me with this task I have to do.'

Simon was silent. Then he spoke 'I'd give my right arm to be by your side. Surely you know that! It's just that it's so difficult right now. My business is growing. I'm taking delivery of a new boat next week. My boys are so young. Sarah hates it if I go away and to cap it all Irena has started having fevers and Sarah thinks it's quite serious. Why did you have to need me now?'

'When you have a family to care for there is never any time that will be more right than another' agreed Jesus 'Let's not worry about it now. If it's meant to happen it will. Let's leave it in God's hands.'

The boat was bobbing in the water shaded by the trees that grew close to the quay. The lake itself shimmered white and silver as the sun rose in the sky and the two men went companionably to their tasks. By midday Simon was fast asleep in the bottom of the boat and Jesus sat alone gazing out across the lake to the hazy purple of the hills beyond. The beauty of the scene pierced his heart. He put his shawl over his head and prayed.

The sun was quite low in the sky when Simon awoke and the two men hurried to his house to wash and tidy up before going to the synagogue. Irena was at the door

'Take your shoes off before you come in' she demanded fiercely.

'This is my house woman!' growled Simon obediently bending down to unfasten his shoes.

'You're not the one who's just spent a day cleaning it' retorted Irena. She bought a bowl of water 'Wash quickly and there's a fresh robe on the chair. You're going to have to hurry if you want to get to the synagogue before sun down!'

Simon pulled Jesus forward. 'You remember Jesus, don't you, my old friend?'

Irena peering into Jesus' face and just for a moment her eyes softened 'Yes' she said 'I remember. I'm not in my dotage yet!'

She took Jesus' hand 'How is your mother?' she said 'I often wonder about her.'

'She's well Irena' said Jesus 'she doesn't leave Nazareth too much now, but she's very content.'

'Hmm!' she replied peering again at his face 'You're older!' she grunted.

'Well yes' Jesus agreed with a smile 'I believe I am.'

'Well hurry on up' she said giving them both a shove 'I've still got a few minutes to finish off the food.'

It was only a short walk to the synagogue and from all over the town men were slipping out of their houses and making their way through the narrow streets. The synagogue itself was an imposing building built on a platform of boulders and standing higher than the rest of the town. It had been build fairly recently on the orders of the Roman centurion whose grand residence overlooked the town from the hills behind.

He was a just man and kept good order and the people of Capernaum had every reason to be grateful to him. Rumours of local despots and unreasonable shows of force often reached their ears from other parts of Galilee and beyond but here in Capernaum, at least, all was well. It was certainly unusual for a Roman officer to give the gift of a synagogue to a community but it was an imposing building in it own right and gave the town status. The people of Capernaum were proud it graced their town.

'There's Philip' Simon pointed to his friend waiting on the steps leading to the large entrance. 'I wonder who he's talking to. I don't recognise him.'

Jesus didn't reply but joined the men as they climbed the steps.

He went directly to Philip and took him by the hand. 'I'm glad you're here Philip' he said and turning to the other man he greeted him with a hand clasp and a kiss. 'It's good to meet you Nathaniel' he said with a welcoming smile 'I need a man like you who is open and honest and who has no truck with deceit.' The man looked puzzled.

'How do you know me?' he asked.

Jesus laughed at his bewilderment 'When Philip found you this afternoon you were sitting under a fig tree outside your house. I saw you then.'

'But you can't have done' Simon blurted out 'You were on the boat with me.'

'I saw him' said Jesus firmly 'And God reminded me that it's not just my old friends that can be trusted. Good can be found in strangers too!'

Nathaniel looked into Jesus' eyes 'Philip believes you to be the Messiah. I'm inclined to think he might be right!'

'Because I saw you under the fig tree?' said Jesus with a smile 'Come! You will see far greater things than that.'

Inside the synagogue the four men stood together and watched with all the others while the sun sank below the western horizon and darkness brought in the Sabbath. They listened as the cantor sang the song of welcome and they all joined the chorus of praise.

The deeply moving service always affected the men and many found they had lumps in their throats and a tear in their eye as the last note faded away.

After the service Philip took Nathaniel to his home while Jesus walked home with Simon.

In the house the little boys excitedly greeted their father and his friend 'Shabbat Shalom Papa' they called out jumping up and down.

'Shabbat Shalom Micah and Joshua!' Simon growled affectionately while his eyes were drawn across the candlelit room to his Sarah. She stood by the table, soft and pretty and petite, her eyes shining with love and welcome and her dark hair loose about her shoulders.

'Shabbat Shalom Sarah!' he said with a catch in his voice and pride in his eyes.

'Shabbat Shalom Simon' she replied quietly and looking beyond her husband to his friend still in shadow by the door. 'Shabbat Shalom Jesus! Do come in. It's good to see you again!'

Jesus walked across the room and took her hands in his and bent forward to kiss her cheek. 'It's very good to be here with you Sarah. Thank you for allowing me to share your Sabbath.'

Irena bustled in to the room 'Come on! Come on!' she urged. 'Simon you haven't said the blessing!'

Simon looked around the room. He stood straight. 'The Lord bless you and keep you; the Lord make his face to shine upon you and be gracious unto you, the Lord turn his face upon you and give you peace.' His deep voice resonated around the room and even the little boys were silenced.

'That's better!' said Irena breaking the spell 'Now take your places.' She pushed her daughter to the head of the table 'It's your turn' she urged her.

Sarah took a taper and turned to one of the lamps on the wall. A flame of light flickered and she lit the two candles on the table.

Her soft gentle voice spoke the familiar words 'Blessed art thou, O Lord our God, king of the universe, who has sanctified us by your commandments and commanded us to kindle the Sabbath light.'

The room sparkled and gleamed in the soft lamp light and everyone stood still hardly daring to breathe as if somehow, if they didn't move, the moment would last for ever.

'Sit! Sit!' demanded Irena impatiently. Everyone looked at each other and grinned. They sank down on the cushions eager for the meal, content with each other's company.

Simon caught Jesus' eye. The look he gave seemed to be both a question and a plea. 'Surely it can't be now. Not now!'

Everyone except Irena went to the synagogue the next morning. 'I'll stay at home' she said firmly 'I'm feeling tired. I'll just sit in the courtyard for a while.'

The little boys looked smart in new sandals and with their hands and faces scrubbed clean. They proudly walked on either side of their father as he and Jesus went in through the main entrance. Sarah joined a friend and slipped in to the women's corridor where they were separated from the men by a separate grill.

Philip and Nathaniel were already inside and had been joined by Andrew who edged over to Jesus as he entered. 'John and James are joining us and should be here soon' he said as he looked towards the door 'Here they are now!'

John and James squeezed through the standing men to join them. Jesus took them by the hand 'A Sabbath day's journey?' he questioned with a quizzical grin.

'We have long legs and take long strides' replied James in a tone that said "Don't question further."

'I'm glad you're here anyway' said Jesus 'Thank you.'

A noise from the back disturbed everyone. Heads swivelled round and then back again 'It's only Samuel' the words were whispered along the line of men. 'He's usually pretty quiet in synagogue' said Philip 'Something must have upset him!'

The chazzan entered and the men took their shawls and put them over their heads as the prayers started.

Sarah watched her boys anxiously, peering through the screen which separated them. She always worried about how they would behave. Another disturbance from the back barely warranted a look. Everyone knew Samuel. He was harmless but he could be noisy. Of course he was often an embarrassment to his family but on the whole he was not dangerous. The demons that possessed him were benign.

The highlight of the service was the opening of the Ark. Capernaum was a wealthy synagogue and had several scrolls. A scroll was selected and carried through the gathered men. As the scroll passed, men reached out to touch it if they could, or at least to touch the clothes of those who carried it. Everybody turned to follow the scroll with their eyes; they must never turn their back on the Torah.

Finally, having completed the circuit, the scroll was placed on the reading desk and the chazzan stepped forward to read. It was the scroll of Jeremiah and the chazzan read

'This is the covenant which I will make with the house of Israel after those days, says the Lord; I will put my law within them, and I will write it upon their hearts; and I will be their God, and they shall be my people.'

When he had finished reading the chazzan invited everyone to sit down.

'We've read that passage many times' he said to the sea of upturned faces 'what a wonderful picture it portrays! A day when all our people know the law by heart. Rabbi Shmole tells us that this means that it is God's will that we extend our synagogue schools. He believes that it is not good enough that we just teach our children to read the Torah; they must learn it by heart. Only then will God's kingdom come on earth.'

An elderly man in the front row spoke up 'We heard that Rabbi Gamaliel believes that we can all be like the scribes and Pharisees and wear phylacteries when we pray. Then the law will be physically close to our hearts and minds. However much we want to we can't be expected to learn all the laws. At least if we do this it will show good intention.' There were murmurs of agreement from among the men. The chazzan looked around and his eyes alighted on Jesus who sat listening intently, surrounded by his friends.

'My friend' said the chazzan 'Are you a learned man? Do you have anything to say?'

Jesus got to his feet and the men looked up expectantly.

His demeanour was still and his stillness calmed the congregation. Nobody moved or fidgeted. A silence filled the building.

'The way God writes in our heart' he said with authority 'is to fill our hearts with his love. If we are filled with the love of God we will act as God acts and think as God thinks. We will not need even to read the laws, let alone learn them, because we will know them.'

He looked around him.

'You are all God's people. He is your God. He has known each one of you from before you were born. He loves you as a father loves his child and He forgives your sins as a father forgives his child's mistakes. He watches over you and he worries over you. He loves each one of you. If you allow that love to fill your hearts you cannot help but live that law.'

The silence was intense. Men looked at each other in amazement but before anybody could speak the noise from the back erupted again. This time a man broke loose from the arms of those who restrained him. He leapt out of the shadows and lunged forward. The men sitting on the floor scrambled to get out of his way.

His arms flailing wildly the man rushed at Jesus. 'Why have you come here Jesus of Nazareth?' he screamed 'I know who you really are! You are God's son.'

An audible shudder went through the building.

Jesus stood his ground and looked directly into the man's eyes. 'Be silent!' he said firmly. 'Leave this man in peace and come out of him!'

The man shuddered and a guttural scream seemed to rise from deep in his body and fill the building. He fell to the ground, twitched and lay still.

The congregation dared not speak.

Jesus reached down and took the man by his hand. 'Come on Samuel' he said with a voice full of compassion 'Go back to your family. You will not be troubled any more.'

An elderly man came forward, tears streaming down his face 'My son!' he said looking around him in bewilderment 'My son!' he repeated and gathered the younger man in his arms.

The congregation erupted 'Who is that man?'

'He is staying with Simon.'

'Did you see what he did?' 'Did you hear how he spoke?' 'What authority!' 'He even commanded evil spirits and they obeyed him.' The synagogue became alive with speculation.

Jesus looked at the chazzan who caught his eye and gave an imperceptible nod.

Reaching for his gavel the chazzan brought it down with a sharp bang on the reading desk. All eyes turned to the front 'The service is ended' he said firmly. 'Return to your homes. Shabbat Shalom!'

'Shabbat Shalom' they all replied obediently and then turned as a man to look for Jesus once again. They looked in vain. He was nowhere to be seen.

CHAPTER FOUR

When the family returned they found Jesus sitting hidden by the back wall, and looking out on the lake. His face was drawn and pale.

They looked at him perplexed, not knowing what to say. He looked up at them and smiled wryly. 'Don't look so worried' he said 'I'm only a bit tired.'

Sarah stepped forward and took his arm. 'Come inside!' she said 'I'll get you a fresh drink and something to eat.'

She looked around. 'Where's mother?' she asked Simon 'She's usually here to organise us the minute we get back.' She turned to the boys 'Go and find your Grandmother will you? She may have dropped asleep in the yard.'

As the boys ran off Sarah led the men into the house. A sudden shout from Joshua startled them.

'Mother, come quickly!'

In the yard they found Irena. She was on the ground slumped against the stone wall of the animal shed. Her eyes were closed and sweat was pouring down her sheet white face. As Sarah knelt beside her and took her hands Irena's body shook violently.

'Oh mother!' cried Sarah in distress. She clutched the older woman to her chest 'What is the matter?'

Simon looked at Jesus 'This has happened before' he said 'and when the fever is over she's left with a terrible headache that lasts for days.'

Jesus reached forward and touched Sarah's shoulder. 'Sarah' he said gently 'Will you trust your mother to me?'

She looked up with tears in her eyes.

'Can you help?' she pleaded anxiously.

'I can' he replied 'Why not go and get the meal ready and leave me here with her. We'll both be hungry very soon!'

A frown creased Sarah's forehead but she got to her feet and Simon led her into the house.

Left alone with Irena Jesus sat on the ground next to her and, taking her hand, began to talk quietly. As he talked Irena slowly began to stop shaking. Soon the tension eased from her body and she became still.

Jesus continued to talk quietly and after a while Irena's eyes opened and she turned her head to look into his eyes. 'Irena you have spent your whole life giving love,' Jesus said 'You care for everybody you meet. If you give so much there comes a time when your body has no strength left with which to do battle when infection comes. You must stop occasionally and allow the love of God to fill your soul and replenish your strength. You will remember that won't you?' he smiled into her face.

As though hypnotised she looked back steadily 'I will' she said 'I will. I'll make time!'

Jesus lifted up her hand 'You are now well again Irena. This illness will not return. Just remember you are greatly loved. It will always give you strength.'

He got to his feet and gently pulled her up 'I'm hungry' he said 'How about you?'

She steadied herself 'I wouldn't have believed it possible, but I am too!' she laughed 'You really are an amazing young man!'

She peered into his face. 'You look tired too! What have you been up to?' she demanded.

'We're quite a pair aren't we?' he laughed.

'After we've eaten you are going to have a sleep' she said firmly. 'And that's an order! Now come and eat!'

He slept all afternoon while the family gathered on the roof top and talked. Andrew, James and John joined them. Occasionally a neighbour would call up to them to ask if the Rabbi was still with them but, stunned and bewildered by the turn of events, the family hardly noticed. They talked together in low conspiratorial tones with Irena enthusiastically urging them to thoughts of even more daring possibilities. Every so often one or other of them would sit back and just gaze in amazement at this little firebrand of a woman who only that morning had been so ill.

As the sun went down and the Sabbath day came to an end the town bustled back into life. Confined to their homes all day the people of Capernaum were free once more to visit and to trade.

On the roof the family were startled by a loud knock on the door below and Andrew bounded down the steps, into the courtyard and through the darkened house. Outside in the swiftly darkening street was a man supporting a young woman.

'Is the Rabbi here?' he demanded in a voice high with panic 'My wife is very sick. Can he cure her?'

Andrew hesitated and the man, losing patience, pushed past him into the house. 'Please where is he?' pleaded the man 'She is so sick and I am frightened she's going to die.'

A quiet voice from behind him in the shadow of the room made the man turn quickly 'I'm here!' said Jesus 'Don't worry!'

'Master!' the man was almost crying 'I was in the synagogue this morning and I saw what you did. I've been waiting for hours for the Sabbath to end so that I could bring my wife to you. You can cure her. I know you can!'

Jesus smiled at him 'Your faith has been enough. Look at your wife. Is she not well?'

The young woman had wriggled free of her husband's arms and was standing on her own with shining eyes. Tears streamed down the man's face and he clasped her to him in relief and looked at Jesus 'How can I ever thank you?' he gasped 'If she had died, I would have too.'

He reached for the leather bag hanging around his waist and took out some coins. 'How much should I give you?' he asked.

'It was love that made you bring her to me and it was the love of God that healed her. There is no money on earth equal to that love. Go on your way, give your thanks to God and be happy!'

Stunned the young couple looked at him in silence and then Jesus, with a sympathetic chuckle, said once more 'Go!'

The young couple turned to the door. Suddenly for the first time Jesus seemed to notice the crowd of people who were blocking the door and who were watching him with mouths open in amazement. Mesmerised they parted to let the young couple out but then closed in again, this time clamouring for Jesus. 'Master, my child is sick!'

cried one 'Rabbi please help my father!' 'My son cannot walk' cried a woman.

'Please help!' Arms and voices were raised in anguish and supplication. Jesus lifted up a hand to silence them. 'Be calm' he said 'I will see you all. Be patient! The love of God does not run out. There is enough for you all.'

He turned to Andrew 'Would you and James and John go outside and calm the people down. Tell them to be patient. I will see each and every one.' He turned to Simon who had entered from the courtyard 'Simon' he said 'You stay here with me and Irena and Sarah would you light the lamps? It's getting so dark in here I can't see who I'm talking to!'

Through the night the people kept coming with tales of heartache and misery. Jesus listened and healed, his face becoming almost grey with exhaustion. Irena anxiously watched him from the shadows and if people pushed forward and crowded him she was there in a flash.

'Get back!' she raged 'Give him space, can't you see he's doing his best!'

People were startled by the fierceness in her voice and hurriedly stepped back when she spoke. Jesus smiled at her and went back to the people while Simon stood by his side taking it all in, his eyes rounded with wonder.

At last in the early hours of the morning the last person had been seen and the family staggered wearily to bed. Jesus slept the moment his head touched the ground and Irena carefully pulled a cover over him and stood looking down at him for a moment before putting out the lights and tip-toeing to her own bed.

When dawn heralded the next morning the insistent banging on the door started again. The noise of pushing anxious people woke the family with a start. Simon went quickly to the door and the people surged forward 'Where is he?' 'Where's the healer?' 'He must see my daughter' 'Can he heal my leg?' The pleas were strident but piteous.

Simon had to shout to be heard. 'Stay there!' he ordered. 'Don't come in, my house is too small. I'll fetch him!'

Turning on his heel he hurried back into the house to wake Jesus from his sleep. The bed was empty. The bed had been neatly rolled and the blankets folded. Simon's heart sank 'Surely Jesus hadn't left without a word.' He turned to find Irena 'He's not in his bed Irena. Where is he?'

'I heard him slip out a while ago' she replied calmly. 'Don't worry I expect he just needed time alone.'

'But the people want him' said Simon in despair 'What shall I tell them?'

'Tell them he is gone but that, without doubt, he will be back' she said firmly. 'That will have to be good enough.'

Simon hurried to the door and when he had delivered his message there was a howl of disappointment. He shut the door quickly and leant against it. 'I'm going to find him' he called to Irena 'He can't have gone far.'

Irena didn't reply and Simon, opening the door again and anxiously peering from right to left, slipped out and ran down to the beach. There was no sign of Jesus by the shore. Old Tabitha, setting up her hot bread stall, said that she hadn't seen him.

Simon ran on round the headland but Jesus was not to be seen. Panting he stood still for a moment and then turned slowly round scanning the distant scene. Was that a flash of white on the hill? Peter stopped and stared. It was difficult to see but yes, there it was again. Not a sheep because there would be others. No, definitely, there was a man alone on the hill. Simon ran through the narrow lanes until he came to a rocky foot path leading up the hill. He gasped as he climbed. Jesus must have heard him coming for he was standing quietly waiting when Simon found him.

'Simon!' said Jesus greeting him with a smile. 'This is very early for you!'

'I'm quite used to early mornings' panted Simon. 'Don't forget I'm a fisherman.'

'I know you are' Jesus replied 'I know how much you enjoy it but if you come with me I will make you a fisher, not of fish, but of men!'

Simon stood still 'I wanted to tell you last night' he said eagerly 'I'm going to come with you!'

Jesus smiled.

'You don't look very surprised' grunted Simon 'but I was!' He sat down on a boulder and looked up at Jesus. 'The family say that now Irena is well again they can manage without me. The men I've employed will never dare go against Irena. She can keep them in order and Sarah is convinced she can look after the boys. In fact' he said ruefully 'They've ordered me to go with you!'

'I'm glad' said Jesus 'But Simon it must be what you want. It's not going to be easy and you must be the one who decides, not your family.'

Simon was serious 'Jesus, I know I will make many mistakes but you are my oldest and dearest friend and I want to be there for you!' He stood up and stepped towards Jesus who put his arm around his friend's shoulders.

'Together Simon' he said 'We will bring God's kingdom a little bit closer. Thank you!'

'But now you've got to come home' Simon suddenly remembered why he was there. 'The people all want you. You are a success, it's wonderful!'

Jesus laughed 'No Simon, that's not success. If I spend my life healing the sick I will be too tired even to talk. I came up here to be alone with God and now I know I have to tell the people about His love as well as showing them. I will come back to Capernaum many times but, right now, I mean to go on to other towns.'

Simon looked aghast 'Just as everything is going so well' he groaned and looked up and saw the determined expression on Jesus' face 'Oh well!' he said resigned 'I suppose we better do as you say!'

'Go back and fetch Andrew, John, James, Philip and Nathaniel and tell them to scrub up first and bring them back here. We are going on to Cana to a wedding.' Simon looked glum 'I will wait here for you, cheer up my friend!' Jesus continued 'I know weddings aren't your scene but I promise you we will do some fishing along the way!'

'On the way to Cana?' asked Simon with a puzzled frown 'its miles from the lake!'

Jesus smiled

'You are a fisher of men now!' he said 'Remember?'

CHAPTER FIVE

They arrived in Cana in the middle of the day and as they entered the village Jesus led his friends off the narrow path to a small square house nestled against the hill in the shade of several gnarled old olive trees. Chickens scattered around and a dog ran towards then barking.

At the sound of the barking four small girls ran out of the house towards them. Dressed in their best clothes they laughed and twirled around in front of the young men.

'Jesus!' they shrieked and then looking closer at the group 'James! John! Look at us! We're going to a wedding!'

'So are we, little one!' laughed Jesus scooping one of them up and swinging her around.

'Jesus' called a soft voice from the doorway. A woman stood calmly watching the scene. Contentment shone in her eyes.

Jesus put the child down and walked towards her. He took her hands in his 'Mother!' he said as he leant to kiss her cheek. 'You see. I'm here on time!'

'I knew you would be' she replied 'and you've brought James and John.' She looked across at the others 'and isn't that Simon and Andrew' she paused 'and surely that's not Philip? My goodness how he's grown!'

'And this is Nathaniel' said Jesus drawing his new friend forward.

Mary took Nathaniel by the hand 'Any friend of my son is a friend of mine' she smiled.

'I suppose this means that it has begun' she said quietly.

'Yes mother it's started!' agreed her son.

'Take care of yourself' she said 'you're very precious to me you know. Don't push yourself too hard.'

'I'll try not to' he agreed with a smile.

'Come and see the bride' Mary said pushing him gently towards the house 'She looks beautiful.'

She did indeed. She smiled up at Jesus as he entered her eyes brimming with joy.

'Oh little Hannah' said Jesus 'are you really old enough to be married? You look so lovely. I hope you are happy.'

'Yes Jesus, I really am!' she looked excited 'and we're going to have the wedding feast in the big house next to the synagogue. Old Jonah has given us permission. We've been cooking for days. It's going to be wonderful!'

'I'm sure it will be' agreed Jesus with a smile. 'What time do we have to go?' he asked.

Hannah's mother came out of the next room.

'We can go right now' she said briskly 'Now you're here Jesus the whole family has arrived. Will you escort your Mother? We'll all walk together down the road. Where's your father Hannah? For goodness sake that man's never here when you need him!'

'Oh yes I am!' cam a voice from the shadows 'I've been ready for ages.'

'Well come on then!' said his wife 'Let's go and find us a son!'

The wedding ceremony went without a hitch. The bride and groom wore crowns of red anemones "Lilies of the Field" the children called them. Mary had brought a beautiful embroidered cloth as a canopy for her niece and her young husband and afterwards the musicians played in the courtyard outside for the young men to form a circle and dance while the girls swayed and giggled to the music and watched the boys.

It was all that Hannah had hoped for and more. Everyone seemed delighted to be celebrating the young couple's love. The wine flowed freely and old Jonah was enjoying being the honoured guest. Even if it was his own house!

All through the afternoon women scurried backwards and forwards from houses in the village carrying platters of food and returning with them empty.

Hannah's father basked in the congratulations, totally unaware of any problems. It was Hannah's mother who first discovered that the wine had run out. In panic she turned to her sister. Mary ran to find Jesus.

She pulled him to a corner so that no-one could hear. 'Jesus the wine has completely run out. What shall we do?'

Jesus looked at her quizzically.

'Don't give me that look son! I know you can help.'

'I could' he said thoughtfully 'but my power is a sacred gift. Should I really use it for something like this?'

'You must decide son' said Mary 'Perhaps you could do it out of love for little Hannah.'

Jesus rolled his eyes to heaven 'You always know the right thing to say' he groaned. Ask my friends to come back to the cellar? And send a few of the servers with some of the empty wine jugs.'

Mary disappeared into the crowd with a smile.

A few minutes later in the cave at the back of the house that served as a cellar, Jesus stood beside six large stone jars. His friends stood by the door way and a few young servers came hurrying in with pottery wine pitchers. Jesus opened the lid of one of the stone jars and told the boys to dip the pitchers in. One by one they came forward and filled their pitchers. They looked bewildered 'But that's water' said one indignantly. 'We can't take that in there to the guests.'

'Dip your finger in and taste it' said Jesus. He looked at them all 'Each one of you. Check if it's fit to serve.'

Each boy did as he was told.

'It's wine!' said the first boy. He turned to Jesus in amazement. 'How did you do that?' he demanded.

'Never mind' said Jesus brooking no more argument. 'Take it to the guests. Fill old Jonah's cup first and then make sure everyone tastes it. I think they will find it good.'

The boys scurried from the room.

Simon strode over to the water jars. He dipped his finger in the wine and tasted it. Then he turned to look at Jesus 'You've done it again!' he exclaimed 'And those fish were no coincidence either!'

Jesus was silent for while.

He walked over to the stone jars and touched one of them 'You see these six jars. They were full of pure water used for our Jewish purification rites. Now they are full of rich, full bodied wine.'

He looked up at his friends.

'Like the jars there are six of you. All from good Jewish stock, brought up by the rabbis to live the Jewish way following a religion that is fine and pure and regulated by the minutest of laws which govern every moment of your lives. But now' he paused throwing wide his arms 'Now, like these water jars, you have begun a new life; a life filled with the new bubbling wine of love. All that the rabbis have taught, has, like the water, been pure and sacred, but I offer you life, life that is full to over flowing with love and joy, and this miracle is to be a sign to you.' He paused again 'The first of many signs.'

***

When the young couple were safely escorted to their new home Mary and her family decided to walk back to Nazareth. It was late and the stars filled the clear sky.

'I want to find Thomas' said Jesus as he walked alongside his mother.

'He doesn't come home during the week' she replied. 'There is so much work at Sepphoris that he stays there and only returns to Nazareth at weekends. Your brothers do the same' she added.

'I'll walk over to Sepphoris tomorrow' Jesus decided. 'It'll be good to see how the building is progressing and how the boys are getting on. If I take the others with me we might stay and help with the work and all come home together in time for Sabbath.'

'You'll need to take food with you. I'll get some ready in the morning' said Mary 'and I'll make up some syrup for Joses, his wife says he has a nasty cough.'

'We won't leave until the third hour' replied Jesus 'Will that give you enough time to get everything ready?'

'I'll have it ready by then' Mary agreed. She looked around contentedly. 'Look at those stars Jesus! What a beautiful night it is!'

'The night you were born' she mused 'was a night like this. The sky was so clear and one star, in particular, was so bright it outshone all the others. I've looked for it every year at the same time but I've never seen it again. It's very strange!'

***

The city of Sepphoris was being rebuilt. The old city had lost the battle against the advancing Roman troops years ago and Herod Antipas, when he had been made tetrarch of Galilee, had moved his capital to the newly built city of Tiberius. Now he wanted to restore Sepphoris to its former glory and make it his capital once more.

Carpenters and builders from all over Galilee had been called in to work on the project. For many it had been their first experience of work and they would know no other until they retired.

The family of Joseph of Nazareth had all worked at the site, even James, who was now studying in Jerusalem, had worked there during his teenage years for you could not be accepted to sit at the feet of a rabbi unless first you had mastered a trade. Jesus, too, had worked long hard days at Sepphoris. When his father had died it was essential to keep the money coming in. With four younger brothers and two sisters to support he had been glad of the work.

Building with stone as well as wood and working outside in all weathers the men were tough and skilled.

As Jesus and his friends topped the ridge and walked down into Sepphoris several workers lifted a hand in comradely salute. Jesus was known and respected.

He knew exactly where to find his family and after brotherly slaps on the back and boisterous greetings he proudly walked around the building inspecting their work. Joses, Judas and Simon, all married now with families of their own, were skilled craftsmen and their work was a credit to them.

The food Mary had sent was welcome too, and, knowing that with extra willing hands to help they could easily make up time, the brothers laid down their tools and took a break.

As they were eating and exchanging family news a lone figure came towards the group. Dressed, as all of them, with his white shift pulled up between his legs and tucked into his leather belt he was solid muscle, broad shouldered and tough.

Jesus stood up and watched him approach 'Thomas' he called 'I came looking for you!'

A man of few words Thomas smiled his welcome and clasped Jesus roughly to him. 'What's this we've been hearing about you?' he asked. 'Some men came up from Capernaum yesterday and told us some very strange things.'

'They're all true Thomas' enthused John. 'You should have been there. So many people were healed!'

'The people crowded round just to see him or touch his robe!' added Andrew 'He's the Messiah all right!'

Thomas frowned at John and Andrew 'It's wild exaggerations like that that will fuel the rumours. You should be more careful!'

'It is true' said Simon 'I didn't believe I would ever say such a thing but if you had been there you would say the same.'

Thomas was silent. He looked at Jesus 'Is this it then?' he questioned 'has it really started?'

'Yes Thomas, it has!' replied Jesus looking directly into his eyes. 'The time is now. Will you be joining us?' Thomas hesitated only for a moment 'I always said I would' he agreed 'I'm not a married man so I have no one to hold me back. It seems I've missed the first couple of days but you can be sure I won't miss any more. I've been waiting since we were children together for this moment. Of course I'm with you!'

The delight on Jesus' face was clear for all to see. 'Come on then' he said, once again the head of the family and leader of the work force. 'For the next few days we build for Herod and then when we go from here, we will build for God.'

CHAPTER SIX

The synagogue in Nazareth was a small square building attached to the rabbi's house. Carpets covered the rough stone floor and stone benches lined the walls. The rabbi himself was elderly. When he had come to the village as a young man he had taught Jesus, his brothers and Thomas to read and write and learn the scriptures. They had all become Sons of the Law under his tutelage. Now, as he looked at these tall young men who came with their friends to the Sabbath day service and filled the little synagogue with their presence, he felt old.

Strange rumours had filtered their way from Capernaum and he eyed Jesus nervously.

He looked around the room. It was unusually full. There were men there that morning he only ever saw at special festivals. Talking quietly among themselves they too glanced repeatedly at Jesus. The atmosphere was tense.

The chazzan, already robed and ready to start the service, edged over to where Jesus was sitting 'Will you read?' he whispered. Jesus nodded.

A sense of normality returned as the service got under way. The prayers were read and the benedictions and psalms chanted. Then the Ark was opened and a scroll removed and held up to the assembled men. The room was too small for the attendant to walk the scroll around, so it was taken directly to the reading desk.

Jesus rose to his feet and went forward. He took hold of the scroll in both hands and rolled it open. It was the scroll of the prophet Isaiah and taking his time he calmly found the column he wanted. The waiting men were silent. Nobody moved or fidgeted. The women in the small room peered through the window. Before he started to read Jesus looked up and saw his mother's usually calm eyes flicker with anxiety.

He began to read.

'The Spirit of the Lord is upon me, because he has anointed me to preach good news to the poor.

He has sent me to proclaim release to the captives

And recover the sight of the blind; to set at liberty those who are oppressed; to proclaim the acceptable year of the Lord.'

Then he closed the scroll and gave it back to the attendant and sat down on the seat next to the reading desk.

The eyes of all in the synagogue were fixed on him. Nobody spoke.

Then he said, 'Today, in your hearing, this scripture has been fulfilled.'

The silence continued and then the old rabbi leant forward 'My son' he said 'that passage has always been held to foretell the coming of the Messiah.'

'Yes' agreed Jesus 'it does!'

Another elderly man spoke up 'I grew up with your father young man. He was an honest hard working man but he was just an ordinary man and didn't pretend to be anything more. Are you claiming to be more than your father?'

'I too am an ordinary man' said Jesus with a smile.

'Ordinary men can't cast out evil spirits or heal the sick' called out another younger man. 'When Simon came back from the market he said that everyone's talking about what you did in Capernaum.'

'Jesus has always been hard working, like his father.' Nahum, a large man with a kindly smiling face spoke up 'I think it wonderful that a man from Nazareth should be able to do such things.'

'Are we sure he can?' asked a younger man more belligerently. He turned to Jesus 'Do a miracle now. Show us!'

Jesus remained calm. 'From what we have read in the scriptures none of the prophets were accepted by their own people. When you return to your roots it is almost impossible to be seen as anything other than the child you were when you grew up.'

'Don't avoid the question!' called out another young man. 'You can't stand up and claim to be the Messiah and then not give us proof!'

'Aren't we good enough for you then?' shouted his neighbour. Jesus looked shocked 'It was in this village that I learnt all about human love' his voice broke 'I thought that at least here you could trust me.'

'Show us a miracle, then we'll trust you!' the young man demanded.

Jesus was silent.

The old rabbi leant forward 'can't you just do something? They're beginning to get angry.'

'No!' said Jesus firmly. 'My power comes from God. Are you asking me to put him to the test?'

'No! No!' said the old man hurriedly. 'No I would never do that!'

An older man, with snow white hair and a long, straight nose spoke carefully. 'I think,' he said 'that what this young man has implied is tantamount to blasphemy. He has all but claimed to be the Messiah and he has compared himself with the prophets. Is there no end to his arrogance?'

'Yes! It's blasphemy!' voices began to be raised. The younger men moved imperceptibly to group together 'If we're not good enough for you, we don't want you here!' one of them called.

Joses was indignant 'He has as much right to be here as you' he retorted 'He has lived here all his life.'

'He wasn't born here though' another young man shouted. 'There was something strange about his birth. I remember my grandmother telling me!'

'That's right!' several voices agreed.

'Get out of here Jesus' called another 'Take your friends with you. We don't want to know whatever it is you have to tell us!'

'It's better that you go' agreed the rabbi 'At least until their anger dies down.'

'Yes, I will go!' said Jesus sadly. 'God's word is too precious to be trampled underfoot like this.'

He stood up and his brothers and his friends scrambled to their feet and moved in close as if to protect him. Together they walked to the door and the men of the synagogue parted to let them through.

Mary hurried to join them in the street, her face was white and drawn. She reached out to Jesus. 'My son! How could they treat you so? I think my heart will break' she cried.

'No mother, it won't!' he smiled sadly 'I'm going away.' He pulled his brothers forward 'The boys will look after you.' He shook his head 'I wanted too much for those I have loved to hear God's word. Perhaps they will one day but I won't come back here again. Look for me in Capernaum. Soon!'

He clasped her to him and stroked her hair. She looked up at him with tears in her eyes 'Go with God, my son!' she said.

Simon rushed forward 'I think now is a good time to go!' he said urgently. 'Those young hot heads are working themselves up into a frenzy.' He caught Jesus' arm. 'Come on my friend. You can't win them all!'

They took the path out of the village back towards Cana but, just as they reached the sharp turn by the escarpment, a group of young men, who had broken away from the others, caught up with them.

'That's right!' they shouted 'Get out!'

One of them picked up a stone and Jesus turned calmly to face him. 'Put that stone down James' he commanded.

The young man hesitated and then he flushed and sheepishly dropped the stone.

The two groups of young men stood and looked at each other in silence and then Jesus strode forward, on and up the hill and out of the village.

Andrew and John, standing together, looked after him. As the wind caught Jesus' cloak and whirled it upwards and the dust whipped around his feet the two men exchanged a glance.

'Come on!' said Andrew to the others 'We'll be hard pressed to keep up with him. He can move like the wind!'

The way to Capernaum passed through several small hill villages before descending to the lake side at Magdala. People who were standing outside their homes in the afternoon sun turned and stared as they passed. It was still the Sabbath and, in the hill villages, in particular, the people were disapproving of the young men travelling away from their home. But Jesus barely noticed them. Lost in his own thoughts he kept up a steady pace and his friends had to run to keep up.

At last, just before the road turned down to the lake, Jesus stopped and sat on a flat rock with the setting sun bathing the purple hills all around with a tinge of vermillion. His friends, gasping a little, were glad to join him.

'That was a bitter pill to take' said Jesus ruefully 'to be rejected like that is hard. It hurts all the more because I believed the people of Nazareth to be my friends. Rejection by strangers will, I fancy, be a little easier to take.'

'Not everyone felt the same' said Thomas 'I'm sure that there are many feeling very ashamed right now.'

'Yes, I know you are right, but I must go on now and get on with the work. We will go back to Capernaum. It will be a good place to make our base for a while.' He looked at Simon with a smile 'I'm looking forward to Irena's cooking again' he laughed.

None of them had noticed the beggar approach them and they looked up suddenly when, instead of coming close, he stood and rapped on a boulder with his heavy walking stick.

'I can't come any closer' he shouted 'but I want to speak to him!' He lifted his stick and pointed it at Jesus.

Jesus stood up. James caught his arm, 'He's a leper. Don't go to him!'

Jesus turned his heard 'Don't worry James' he said and walked purposefully over to the man.

'What can I do to help you?' he asked looking with pity at the man's disfigured face.

'If you wanted to you could cure me' the man was abrupt and his tortured eyes were turned in hope towards Jesus.

'If I wanted to?' questioned Jesus taken aback. 'What makes you think I wouldn't want to help?'

'I'm a leper!' the man was defiant 'We are shunned by everyone.'

Jesus moved closer, he eyes dark with compassion. He put out a hand and touched the leper's arm. The man shuddered and James drew in his breath.

'Of course I want to make you better' said Jesus still touching the leper's arm. He spoke with a voice thick with emotion and then he closed his eyes and stillness enveloped his body. When he opened his eyes again he said quietly 'Be well again.'

Thomas stepped closer and as they all watched with eyes growing wide with wonder the leper's skin healed before their eyes.

The leper too watched as new skin replaced the old and his disfigurement melted away. Tears of joy began to run down his face.

'Now I will be able to see my children again' he cried 'it has been hell to be so rejected and despised.'

He looked up at Jesus 'How can I ever thank you?' he asked through his tears.

'Before you go to your family' said Jesus 'you should go the priest to verify the cure and offer the required sacrifice in thanks to God.'

'It is God we must both thank' continued Jesus taking the man's hands in his. 'This morning I too suffered rejection and hurt, but my hurt was as nothing compared to yours.' He pushed the man gently away.

'Go now!' he said 'Go and live and be happy!'

Speechless with gratitude, the man spun on his heels and ran towards the town. Eventually finding his voice he called back over his shoulder 'I won't forget!' he cried.

Jesus laughed and turned to his friends 'It's been a strange day' he said 'and we are all tired! Thank you for standing by me. It would have been hard without you. But go down to Capernaum now. Go to your homes and rest and I will meet you at Simon's house in the morning.'

He did not need to tell them that he wanted to be alone. They already understood that to Jesus prayer was even more necessary than food.

As the men walked away down the darkening, narrow path to the lake road Jesus turned, and lifting his shawl over his head, was silhouetted for a moment as the sun, with one final fiery burst, sank below the horizon. Then, with ever lightening steps, he strode eagerly away from the pathway until he was lost in the shadows of the olive trees.

CHAPTER SEVEN

News that Jesus had returned to Capernaum spread like wild fire. The crowds were already waiting outside Simon's house before even Irena had woken. When she opened the door and saw them all nervously standing around she scowled at them fiercely and like a lioness defending her cub she demanded of them all

'Can't you leave him alone? He's sleeping! You're all wearing him out!'

'No Irena' said Jesus appearing behind her in the door way 'this is the work I came to do. I can not waste too much time sleeping.' He turned to the people 'You are carrying heavy burdens of pain. Come! Now is the time to put the burdens down and rest.'

He put his arms around Irena 'While the others are sleeping I will see them all outside the house.'

Irena looked at him tenderly but nevertheless grunted her disapproval before going back in to the house. She returned minutes later with a stool. 'At least you can sit down' she ordered 'it looks like it's going to be a long day.'

Jesus did as he was told and the people crowded closer.

He listened to their tales, dried their tears, touched their loved ones and healed the sick, his face becoming greyer and more lined with exhaustion as the hours went by and the sun rose in the sky. The crowds around him continued to grow.

When James and John and the others arrived Simon turned to Thomas anxiously 'Every time someone is healed Jesus seems to lose strength. We can't let him go on like this!'

'If he were not sitting down I think he would fall' agreed Thomas. 'I'm going to stop him.' He pushed towards Jesus.

Lifting his eyes Jesus saw him coming. He put up his hand 'Not yet Thomas! I cannot stop now! There is so little time.'

Thomas hesitated and then seeing the determination in Jesus' eyes returned to the others.

Just then a small group of elders from the synagogue appeared in the lane. Out of respect the people parted to let them through. They stood before Jesus, who rose to his feet to greet them. 'Rabbi' they said 'we have come to you on behalf of the Centurion who built our synagogue. He has a much loved slave who is very sick. Indeed he is at the point of death. Can you heal him?'

Jesus looked around at the expectant crowd who were anxiously waiting for his attention and he hesitated. One of the elders urged him further. 'He is a good man and he loves our people. It is unusual to find such a just leader. He truly is worthy of your intervention.'

Jesus smiled a little wearily 'I will come' he replied and got up from his seat. Irena was already there with his cloak and, as he followed the elders, many of the crowd followed him as if reluctant to let him out of their sight.

They had already left the town and were climbing the hill toward the centurion's house when a young Roman officer on horse back came galloping down to meet them. Bringing his horse to a hurried halt he dismounted quickly and came to Jesus.

'Sir' he said 'my master has asked me to say that it is not necessary for you to come into his house. He knows that to do so will cause you to break with your traditions. He says that he knows what it is like to have authority. He gives orders and knows they will be obeyed to the letter. He has told me to tell you that he recognises that you too have great authority' he looked at Jesus intently 'he says that all you need to do is to say the word and he knows his slave will be healed.'

Jesus was surprised 'I did not expect to find so much faith in one who is not a Jew' he said to the elders. 'This Gentile is an example to us all.'

Turning back to the young officer he said 'Go back to your master. His slave has been healed.'

The young man saluted Jesus and giving a short bow from the waist, he mounted his horse once more, whirled it around and returned to the centurion's house.

Many in the crowd wanted to go up to the house to see if a miracle had indeed occurred but Jesus had already turned and was heading back in to the town. They hesitated for a while and then ran behind him anxious not to let him out of their sight.

Back at Simon's house Irena was brooking no nonsense. 'A meal is ready Jesus. Come in now. You can go back to the people later.'

She turned to John and Andrew 'You two stay by the door. No-one is to come in until he is finished.'

As if realising the sense of her words the crowds sat down patiently to wait. Several of them went down to the quay and bought food from Tabitha and returned to sit in the shade of the high walls of the street while they waited for Jesus to return. The day was hot and sultry.

It started to rain before Jesus had finished eating. Pushing away what was left of his food he went to the door. People were scurrying about looking for shelter and putting cloaks over those too sick to walk. Jesus watched with compassion in his eyes. He turned to Simon 'Can we let them in?' he asked.

Simon glanced at Irena who shrugged her answer and soon the little house was filled to over flowing. It became hot and stuffy, but Jesus seemed to have recovered his energy and began again to call upon the power that God had given him. The numbers of those needing his help didn't seem to get any less even though John and Andrew did their best to encourage people to leave once Jesus had seen them in order to make room for others. Two of the scribes attached to the synagogue pushed their way in to see what was going on and they too were welcomed into the little house.

It was not long after their arrival that those in the room around Jesus suddenly felt a scattering of broken plaster pieces fall about them. Looking up in consternation the whole ceiling seemed to be moving and then a crack appeared, another fall of plaster and then a hole. Daylight streamed in the small opening. The people below watched as eager hands pulled back the plaster and the reeds. Soon the hole was large and faces appeared peering down into the room.

Then before the amazed gazes of all below, a man was lowered roughly through the roof, with two pieces of rope and many willing hands, until he lay on the floor at Jesus' feet.

Even Jesus was startled by the effrontery of the men and if Simon was indignant Irena was almost incandescent with rage!

'What have you done to the roof' she shouted up to the peering faces 'how dare you!'

The men looking down were mortified. Carried away by their desire to get their friend to Jesus they had barely given a thought to the fact that they had damaged someone's house.

They were obviously sorry. 'We will make it good' they promised hastily. 'We couldn't get through the door. There are just too many people.'

Jesus shrugged his shoulders with a smile 'Oh well then' he said ruefully 'you had no choice really did you?'

The tension eased and those in the house began to chuckle. The faces of the men on the roof flushed a deep red. 'We really will mend the hole' said one of the men 'please sir, look at our friend!'

The man at his feet was paralysed from the neck down. He lay awkwardly just as he had been lowered. His hair and clothes were wet from the rain. Those nearby reached out to help straighten his limbs and he smiled his thanks, too scared by all that was happening to dare to speak.

Jesus looked down with compassion 'My son' he said 'your sins are forgiven you.'

Those in the room looked up startled. Their heads turned quickly to see the reaction of the scribes. The two scribes stiffened and became instantly alert.

Jesus too looked round the room and paused for a moment before he spoke again. 'For generations now,' he said 'we Jews have believed that a man who is afflicted as this man is, is being punished by God for some sin he has committed. And if a person is unfortunate enough to be born with these infirmities we say that it is the parents who are being punished. When we see suffering like this we want an easy explanation and punishment for sins fits the bill.'

He looked around once more with his eyes coming to rest on the two scribes. 'And yet I expect' he continued 'that when the religious among you give, as the law commands you, to the sick and the poor you will generously give your coins to sufferers such as this.'

The two scribes nodded their agreement and a murmur of approval rippled through the room.

Jesus spoke again, more firmly, more directly 'And as you do so' he continued 'are you not therefore rewarding the sin? If you believe it is God's punishment, should you be rewarding the sufferers in this way?'

There was confusion in the room and the eyes of the man on the floor filled with tears. Was Jesus going to refuse to heal him?

'That's the argument the Rabbi Gamaliel uses' one of the scribes said puzzled 'he doesn't believe that God punishes in this way.'

'But we don't know' argued the other 'so how can a peasant healer from here in Galilee take it upon himself to tell this man that his sins are forgiven?' He looked accusingly at Jesus 'Remarkable though your healings are it is dangerous to challenge God in this way.'

Jesus was silent. He looked down at the man and then said with compassion in his voice 'All his life this man has been made to believe that some sin, either his or his parents, has been at the root of all his misery. If he continues to believe this he cannot be healed. But God is just and merciful and above all he is loving. Each moment of each day he is forgiving our sins because of this great love.'

He looked up at the man's friends who were anxiously holding their breath. 'Out of love you brought him here' said Jesus 'and through the love of God he will walk from here by himself.'

He leant down and took the man's hand 'To show everyone here the power of God's love. To show you all that this man's sins are forgiven and to show you that God is working now through me' he looked into the man's eyes 'I say to you, get up, pick up your bed and walk home!'

And the man rose. Never before had he stood on his feet and he staggered a little but then, with joy in his eyes, he stood tall and gazed in wonderment around the room. Then he bent down and rolled up his bedding and ran from the room.

In the silence that descended on the room Irena bustled forward 'Don't forget to come back and mend this roof!' she called up wagging her finger at the man's friends. The people in the room dissolved into laughter and the voices of the men could be heard calling out through the general hubbub below 'We promise! We'll be back! Thank the master.'

Then Jesus stood up and put his palm up to the hole in the roof 'I do believe the rain has stopped' he said with a smile. 'I need some fresh air and some time alone.' He turned to look at Simon 'Can we take the boat?'

Simon's eyes lit up 'Yes!' he said, jumping to his feet. 'Yes! I'll go ahead and get it ready' and he ran from the room like an excited child.

As Jesus moved to follow him those still waiting to see him began to wail. He hesitated and then stopped to reassure them 'I will see you tomorrow' he promised 'I will see you all!'

As he walked away from the house his friends scrambled after him.

'Do you want to be alone?' asked Philip 'or shall we come?'

'Come!' said Jesus 'All of you come!'

Two young men stood apart from the others and one of them called to Jesus, 'Jesus last week you cured my mother. Now she is fit and healthy again. I would like to learn more about you. Can I, and my friend, come with you too?'

Jesus smiled 'Come!' he said 'I remember you Thaddeus. You were the one who brought your mother to me. Bring your friend!'

'My name is Simon' called the other 'Son of Alphaeus.' He was eager and ran towards Jesus. 'Are you the one we have all been waiting for? Are you the Messiah?'

'You can watch and listen and make up your own mind. Come!' said Jesus with his face crinkled in amusement. 'The other Simon is a rich man and his boat is large. The air here is still sultry despite the rain. It will do us good to have some fresh air!'

'Rich man indeed!' muttered Simon as Jesus climbed on board. 'Andrew has told me what you said.'

'Can you deny it Simon?' smiled Jesus gently 'You are greatly blessed.'

'That I am!' agreed Simon 'When Sarah agreed to marry me I became the happiest man in the world.' He pushed the boat away from the quay and jumped forward to put up the sail. The wind whirled off the shore and the little red sail billowed out in joy.

Peter's face was a picture. He turned to face Jesus and raised his arms with exhilaration. 'You're right' he shouted 'I'm rich. I'm very rich!'

Everyone laughed with him and the boat sped out towards the middle of the lake. 'Take us over to the other side' called Jesus 'Find a deserted place so that we can be alone.'

He pulled out the cushions from under the seat that he had repaired only the week before and settled down to rest. Within seconds he was asleep oblivious to the contented chatter of his followers and the hard slap, slap of the waves against the sides of the boat as it sped through the water.

The rain clouds still hung low in the sky and as the boat went further out into the middle of the lake the wind grew stronger. 'I think we should put a tuck in the sail Simon' called Andrew who with John was standing in the prow 'We're hitting the waves at quite a rate!'

'Can you and John manage it on your own or do you need help?' shouted Simon.

'We'll manage!' replied Andrew and the two friends clambered back to the mast.

It was a struggle but both Andrew and John were experienced crew and the red sail was soon a great deal smaller. 'That's better!' called Simon 'She's easier to handle now.'

The wind was refreshing and after the stifling heat inside Simon's house the young men felt invigorated. The squall when it came took them all by surprise. A sudden wall of air hit them on the beam and the boat tipped dangerously on to its side. James and Philip were thrown across the deck and fell awkwardly against Nathaniel in a tangle of ropes. Water washed over the side and the boat seemed to take an age to right itself again. When it did Simon shouted at them all 'Bale the water out as quickly as you can. If that happens again we're done for!'

He pulled on the tiller and tried to turn the boat into the wind 'She won't come round!' he roared.

'I think the wind is changing direction' called James urgently.

'These lake storms are so unpredictable!' yelled Simon 'just keep baling all of you!'

The waves were higher now and water continually slopped over the gunwales. Everyone bent to the task. 'It's no good Simon' called Andrew 'It's coming in as fast as we're getting it out.'

As he spoke the wind hit again, this time from the stern. The boat shot forward and a wave rolled under the stern and lifted the boat on its crest so that it careered forward at an alarming rate.

The men dropped their balers and clung on for dear life.

Above the noise of the wind Andrew screamed to his brother 'Wake Jesus!'

'Oh my God!' exclaimed Simon 'He's still sleeping!' He turned to where Jesus lay and grabbed him fiercely by his arm. 'Wake up Jesus! Wake up! We're sinking!'

Jesus sat up and his eyes opened in amazement when he saw the storm. 'You should have woken me earlier' he said and catching hold of a stay he pulled himself to his feet. He stood for a moment while the boat, at the mercy of the wind and waves, continued to roll forward dangerously.

John grabbed Andrew's arm 'Look at Jesus!' he shouted above the noise of the storm. 'Look at him!'

Andrew stood rigid with fear.

A strange light surrounded Jesus as he stood in the stern and his black eyes were as fierce as fire.

As the others in the boat turned and gazed in wonder Jesus lifted his hand and pointed at the blackest of the storm clouds.

'Peace!' he ordered 'Be still!'

And the wind died away and a deep calm descended.

Nobody moved. Nobody spoke.

Then John whispered into Andrew's ear 'Did you see his eyes? That is how he was when he came out of the desert!' Andrew nodded, his eyes wide and fearful. He couldn't speak. 'I don't think I'll be scared of anything else, ever again!' John sank down on the seat behind him.

With his eyes still black with fire Jesus looked at them all. 'You did not need to be afraid' he said sternly. 'Where is your faith?'

The men were silent. Their wet hair and clothes clung to their bodies and, still gripping on to the boat for dear life, their knuckles were white with tension. With eyes wide open in awe they began to shiver; not from the cold but from fear.

Simon sank to his knees and gazed in horror at his childhood friend. Who was this man that even the wind and seas obeyed him?

CHAPTER EIGHT

Repairs were needed so the following morning Simon carefully steered the boat on to the muddy stretch of shore near the jetty at Bethsaida. With John and Andrew he proposed to stay there most of the day until he was satisfied that the boat could be safely sailed on to Capernaum.

Jesus and the others set out along the road. Conscious that he had promised the people he would be back, there was more than a sense of urgency in his step. The air was fresh and the water sparkled in the early morning sun. No-one would ever believe that a storm could disturb the tranquillity of such a sea of glass. The young men didn't speak of what had happened but it wasn't something they would easily forget.

There were several people on the road. A shepherd followed by a small flock of sheep and a couple of dogs held everybody up for a while but soon turned off towards the hills. A man almost bent double with a sack of grain came towards them out of Capernaum and greeted Jesus with great respect, and small groups, recognising Jesus, just stopped and stared as he strode out towards the town.

There was no doubt that he was a young man in a hurry.

Young Simon did his best to keep pace with Jesus. He had so many questions he wanted to ask but Jesus was moving too fast for him to ask them.

When they came to a toll booth on the roadside they were forced to stop and join the queue of men and women waiting to have their names checked against a list of tax payers. The tax official was efficient and people didn't have to wait long. Even the most belligerent were dealt with firmly but kindly.

When Jesus came to the booth the tax collector looked up 'Name?' he asked.

'Jesus, son of Joseph of Nazareth, builder.'

The man ran his finger down the scroll. 'Ah, here we are! Family business, all taxes up to date. You may go!'

Jesus looked at the man 'Are you happy in your work Matthew?'

The man looked startled 'How do you know my name? Have we met before?'

'No!' said Jesus 'we haven't met but I have heard of you. It's not usual to find an honest tax collector assigned to a toll booth.'

'Do you think Marcus Aurelian, our local governor, would have anyone working for him who wasn't honest?' laughed Matthew.

'No I don't' agreed Jesus. 'I've never met him but I've reason to believe him to be a remarkable man.'

'I heard you healed his slave' conceded Matthew looking up at Jesus enquiringly.

'Yes I did!' Jesus did not elaborate but Matthew was interested.

'How do you do these things?' he asked directly. 'I too have heard of you and the things you have done.'

Jesus looked at him 'May I come to your house for a meal tonight' he asked 'I could answer your questions then.'

Matthew looked surprised. He leant back in his chair and looked quizzically at Jesus. 'I'm a tax collector' he said. 'You are a rabbi, are you seriously wanting to come into my house?'

Jesus spoke firmly 'Yes Matthew. I would be honoured to be your guest.'

The young man paused thoughtfully looking long and hard at Jesus 'You're very welcome!' he replied. 'I'll see you tonight.'

Back at Simon's house Irena and Sarah had organised those who were waiting for him. There was no pushing or shoving, just two rows of quietly waiting patients. Jesus was impressed. 'You two are worth your weight in gold' he said warmly 'I'm inclined to believe that my friend Simon is the luckiest man in the world.'

'He certainly is!' laughed Irena 'I wouldn't argue with that.'

The sick were so relieved to have Jesus back among them and they found that being so organised was a comfort. It prevented them from panicking. Jesus was surprised at how many people he was able to help and although he began to feel very tired he realised that he was far less stressed. With the women's help much of the strain had been removed. As the morning drew on a man came forward with his two children, a teenage boy and a young girl. He looked a picture of health and Jesus looked up at him surprised.

'I know you' he said 'at least I'm almost certain I do!'

'You certainly do' said the man with a smile. 'My name is Micah. I look a little different now from the last time you saw me. Then I was dirty and unshaven and very disfigured.'

'You were the leper!' exclaimed Jesus pleased. He looked at the children, 'I'm so pleased to meet you two' he said 'Your father missed you so much.'

'I came to say thank you' Micah was close to tears. 'Being parted from my family was killing me!'

Jesus stood up and put his arm around the man's shoulders. 'You have learnt the most important of all truths;' he said 'You have learnt that love is so powerful it will survive separation, even the separation of death itself.'

'When I was a leper I lived in this other world with lepers and outcasts.' He pointed to the door. 'They are still out there, rejected and unwanted, separated from their families, lost and afraid.' His voice was anguished. 'They are men and women that I have learnt to care for. Please help them!'

Jesus stood back and gazed toward the open door 'You are right!' he mused 'They are indeed the forgotten, invisible children of God!'

He looked at Micah 'Will you take me to them?'

Micah's eyes lit up 'I'll take the children home and come back for you!' he promised. 'Thank you!' he said 'Thank you!'

True to his word Micah did not take long to return. Pleased that Jesus had managed to see all those who had come to the house Irena was anxious and upset when she heard what he planned to do now. She wanted Jesus to rest.

Jesus didn't argue with her but when Micah returned he introduced him to Irena and discreetly left them alone. When they left, although still not entirely convinced,

Irena didn't try and stop them going. They took the road towards Magdala and the hills beyond.

They went alone.

It took them well over an hour to find the group of lepers. Jesus realised that if he had stayed on the road he would never even have known they were there. Micah led him through the scrubby bushes and rough boulders until he reached a low cave. At first there appeared to be no-one around but undeterred Micah called his friends by name. 'Joshua! Miriam! David! Aaron! Come out everyone. It's quite safe!'

Jesus was aware of movement. Then the rocks and the bushes began to come to life and ragged wisps of men and women appeared. Many held cloth in front of their faces so that Jesus could only see their eyes. They were nervous and stayed back, keeping their distance.

Jesus looked at them all and tears appeared in his eyes.

His voice, when he spoke, was thick with emotion. 'The love Micah has for you all has brought me to this place and I have come to bring you the love of God. It is time to lay down the burdens you are carrying!' He raised both his hands and closed his eyes. Visibly drawing on all the strength he could muster he said loudly and clearly 'Be clean and be whole once more!'

Keeping his hands raised he opened his eyes as one by one the lepers watched as their skins and bodies were made whole. Some sank to their knees, tears coursing down their faces. Others leapt and shouted for joy.

Micah was overjoyed and excited for his friends. He ran from one to another hugging and shaking hands.

There was so much excitement, nobody noticed that Jesus had fallen.

When Micah turned and saw what had happened he ran back, consternation on his face. He lifted Jesus from the ground and helped him to a nearby rock. The men he had healed hovered anxiously. Years of rejection had conditioned them to keep their distance and nobody dared move closer. When Jesus recovered he beckoned them all and they edged forward nervously. 'You are all children of God' he said to them, looking into their eyes. 'Stand tall once more. You are very precious in God's eyes: Very precious and much loved.'

They didn't speak. Bewilderment and confusion flickered in their eyes.

Jesus smiled again. 'Go home!' he said. 'Go home to your families, but never forget how precious you are!'

***

When Jesus left that place to return to Capernaum he did not have the strength to clamber over the rocks and Micah had to help him. When they reached the path once more Jesus was still leaning heavily on Micah's arm. The rhythm of walking seemed to help and by the time they reached Capernaum he had recovered enough to walk on his own. His face was pale with exhaustion.

Where the road entered the town a young man suddenly moved away from the wall of a house. He stepped forward as Jesus approached. 'Jesus!' his voice was low and controlled 'I want to become one of your followers!'

Jesus stopped, swayed a little as he strove to keep his balance. Micah discreetly caught hold of his elbow.

Jesus looked at the young man in front of him. He was good looking and lithe and his clothing was expensive and clean. He obviously took pride in his appearance. His eyes were sharp and there was certain intensity about his demeanour.

'I have come' said Jesus slowly 'with only one weapon in my hand: the sword of God's love, and, with love only, my task is to defeat the forces of evil and death.'

He looked at the young man sadly. 'If you become my follower' he said 'do you think you can survive without the dagger you wear under your clothes?'

The young man was startled. 'How did you know?' he exclaimed.

Jesus was silent.

'My name is Judas' the young man continued 'and yes, I am an Iscari! I believe we Jews should fight against those who threaten our freedom. I feel passionately for my country. I am not ashamed of it!'

'Nevertheless' said Jesus 'If you come with me you must leave your dagger behind and learn instead about the weapon of God's love.'

It was Judas' turn to be silent. Then reaching inside the folds of his clothing he took a small dagger from a belt around his waist. He threw it to the ground and grinned up at Jesus. 'Teach me about love!' he demanded.

'I will!' promised Jesus 'Come!'

CHAPTER NINE

As Jesus approached Matthew's house the evening was already drawing to its close and people were making their way home.

Capernaum was a small market town. Everybody knew each other's business and it did not take long for the news that Jesus was visiting the tax collector's house to spread.

Speculation was rife.

Why should a man whose popularity as a new teacher was growing every day, deliberately try to sabotage this success by consorting with a collaborator?

Although Jesus went alone that evening his young followers couldn't help feeling concerned. Not liking to criticise Jesus they were, however, nervous of the crowd's reaction. It was a shock to Judas that the very first thing Jesus had chosen to do after he, Judas, had decided to join the group, was to go and socialise with a man who would previously have been on the Iscari hit list.

Seemingly oblivious to the anxiety, Jesus was enjoying his evening out.

Matthew had greeted him warmly and his servant had been attentive. Although not a married man Matthew's house was well appointed, spacious and immaculately clean. Jesus sat comfortably on the large cushions. A bowl of spicy chicken stew accompanied by a basket of soft bread was placed on the low table between them and a fruity red wine was poured into fine ceramic cups.

Matthew was an easy conversationalist and a well educated man. He was fascinated by Jewish history and the two men found they had a lot to talk about.

It was strange to be talking to a tax collector about the writings of prophets and several times Jesus looked enquiringly at Matthew as if trying to work him out.

Matthew was amused and eventually after a couple of cups of wine he relaxed enough to explain. 'My parents' he said 'worked for the governor who was here before Marcus Aurelian. My father looked after the horses and my mother was the housekeeper. They lived in the servant quarters and I was born there. By the time I was eighteen my father had died and Marcus was the new governor. He soon realised I was quick with figures and before I knew it I took over as the tax collector for Capernaum when old Rueben died.'

He paused, 'My mother still lives up at the Governor's quarters but she's no longer the housekeeper. She does a bit of laundry and cleaning and Marcus says she can stay. He thinks the world of her.'

Jesus looked at him thoughtfully 'You are your own man then?' he enquired 'with no dependants?'

Matthew laughed 'It sounds as though you have a plan for me!'

'Can you read my mind then?' Jesus was smiling broadly.

Matthew looked into Jesus' eyes and his face became serious 'You want me to give up this way of life and follow you.'

'I do' agreed Jesus 'I need a man like you. As far as the people are concerned your profession makes you an outcast, but it has not made you a bitter man. You are well balanced and fair and you are articulate and learned.'

Jesus paused and, leaning forward, spoke again intently. 'My mission will not be a long one' he said. 'The love of God challenges the hearts of all men and evil does not like being challenged. The way ahead will be hard and it will be short.' His fingers caressed the edge of the table and he continued 'When I am gone I will need my followers to pick up my mantle and continue my work. I need my words to be remembered. I have chosen good, faithful men but many of them are not educated as you are.' He looked into Matthew's eyes 'I need you to remember and record my words so that generations to come will be able to learn of the good news I have come to bring.'

Matthew got up from the cushions and began to walk around the carpeted room. He picked up small possessions as he passed and put them down again lovingly. He didn't speak.

When he did he spoke in measured tones. 'Today has been the strangest of days' he said 'When you spoke to me this morning and asked if you could come here to my house for a meal something stirred deep in my heart.' He continued to walk 'It was as though I had been waiting for that moment all my life, and now' he said 'I know why!'

He looked at Jesus 'Would you be surprised to know that I have already informed the Governor of my intention to leave with you? And' he went on 'that I have arranged to have my house and possessions sold?'

Jesus smiled. 'Everything about you Matthew is surprising' he said 'But no! I am not surprised, only very thankful.'

Matthew smiled 'I've arranged for half of the money the sale makes to go to my mother and the rest to be held by trustees to settle any claims any of my clients may have against me. I wouldn't want to think that I had cheated someone and they couldn't receive recompense.'

He drew a deep breath 'Everything I have done in life has always been planned to the tiniest of detail. I am a cautious man by nature but today my world has been turned upside down!'

'Today' repeated Jesus 'Today salvation has come to this house!'

'I have a feeling' added Matthew, 'that my life from now on will be very different indeed!'

'Yes!' agreed Jesus 'that will certainly be so. But now' he said 'I need to tell you about a young Iscari called Judas. I suspect he will find your presence among us a little difficult!'

***

The next morning a small deputation of scribes and elders from the synagogue was waiting for Jesus when he left Simon's house. Their faces were disapproving. 'You are a young teacher and you have become very popular, very quickly' they said. 'We have given you our support so far but we are not happy about some of the things you are doing.'

'Or saying!' added one of the scribes quickly. Jesus turned to look at the speaker. It was one of the two scribes that had been present when he had healed the paralysed man.

'Last night we have heard that you went to the house of Matthew, the tax collector.' The horror in the scribe's voice was plain to hear. 'If you are setting yourself up to be a rabbi and if you want us to continue to support you, you must realise that it is very unwise of you to behave in this way. In fact it's unacceptable.'

Jesus was calm. He smiled at them easily and said 'People who are well do not need the services of a doctor. It is only those who are sick who need to call for a physician.'

'I have come' he said firmly, looking directly into the eyes of the spokesman 'not to call the righteous into God's kingdom for they are already there. I have come instead to call the sinner. I must, therefore, spend my time with sinners.'

'And with the unclean?' asked the same scribe. 'People who have dealings with lepers make themselves unclean.'

'We are all God's children' stated Jesus.

'And you touched them and have not come to the synagogue to use the purifying waters.'

A ripple of shock went through the group and they turned in towards each other to confer.

All of the young men Jesus had collected were gathering around him. Matthew was the last to arrive and as he walked down the road to join the group the religious leaders stared in disbelief.

'I have chosen these twelve men to be my disciples' Jesus said proudly 'And with them we will bring about God's kingdom.'

'With fishermen, builders and tax collectors?' The scribes were contemptuous.

Jesus did not smile. The look he gave them was icy with anger. 'God does not look on the outward part. He looks on the heart!'

He turned to the disciples 'We need to talk. Come! Let us find a quiet place' and without another word he turned and took the path that led to the hill behind the Governor's house.

They gathered around a rocky outcrop at the top of the hill. Black, basalt boulders were scattered everywhere and the first blades of new green grass were pushing their way through the bare soil. The sky was clear and the hills surrounding the lake were already hazy in the heat of the rising sun.

'I have warned you all' said Jesus severely to the gathered men 'that by choosing to stay with me you have chosen the hard way. Already' he went on 'opposition is beginning and it will not become any less. Foxes have holes and the birds of the air have nests but already I have no place to call my home. If you follow me you must be totally committed. It is no good putting your hand to the plough and to be forever turning round and looking behind you. We must all look forward and be firm in our commitment.'

'I need you' he said 'And God has called you. Together we will spread the good news of God's love so that all may enter His kingdom.'

He did not need to ask them to decide yet again. He knew that their hearts were his.

***

It was the children who reached the group first. Running ahead of the adults they rushed excitedly in on the group. Simon and James, realising the seriousness of the moment, jumped up quickly to hold them back and quieten them down but Jesus laughed delightedly at the unexpected interruption.

'No Simon' he said 'let them be. Young children are innocent and trusting. The kingdom of Heaven belongs to them. We have much to learn from children' he reached out to tousle a young ruffian's hair and pick up a small girl and put her on his knee. 'If we can trust with a childlike innocence we too will enter the kingdom.'

The adults were not long in joining the group and as they arrived they sank relieved but exhausted on to the ground. The children were quickly called back to parents and made to sit and behave.

Looking down the hill the disciples could see people streaming out of the town and making their way up the small paths. They looked at Jesus enquiringly.

He smiled ruefully 'We didn't go far enough away to be alone but never mind, away from the synagogue I can speak more clearly about what is on my mind.

They waited quietly for the crowds to arrive and settle and then Jesus stood up on his rock and the crowd grew silent.

He looked around at them all, the poor, the hard working, the religious, the doubting, the sorrowful, the young, the old and his heart went out to them all.

'God has blessed you all' he said and his voice carried in the still morning air. 'Even those of you who feel that life is hard! You particularly have a special blessing because in the loneliness of your distress you realise that no-one can help you save God alone and so in the darkness you call to him. In that moment, when all your defences are down, you come closer to God than you ever have before.'

'The arrogant that never know failure or doubt never know their need of God and are never able to get close to him.'

'But you, the poor in spirit, the mournful, the seekers, you are truly blessed because you have called to God and he has come close to you.'

The crowd gazed up at him with rapt attention. 'Let your religion be simple and pure. When you pray, talk to God in private, don't show off your piety in order that people are impressed. When you give alms or fast, other people don't need to know what you are doing. Your faith is between you and God. Learn to love God as He loves you. That is true religion.'

A woman called out from the crowd 'Jesus teach us how to pray! Praying is hard and I don't know what to say.'

Jesus smiled at the interruption. 'When you pray' he said 'remember that God has known you from before you were born. You are his child and He loves you and wants you to talk to Him.'

He looked around 'Let us be practical' he said 'If you meet a respected friend you greet him don't you? Very well then you begin by greeting God but remember He loves you as His child so say "My Father!" And then give the honour he is due say "My Father in heaven, hallowed be your name, may your kingdom be established here on earth just as it is in heaven."

'Then' said Jesus 'tell God what is on your heart and ask for his help. Ask him too to forgive your sins. But' and Jesus looked around again 'you cannot expect God to forgive your sins if you cannot be forgiving of others. And finally, having been assured of forgiveness, you must beg God to give you the strength not to sin again.'

'This will give you a pattern for prayer.' He looked at the woman 'But it is important to speak what is on your heart. God is not impressed by long prayers which are just meaningless words.'

'But the scribes and the Pharisees and the elders in the synagogue are all righteous men. They are religious. Their prayers are long, they fast, they tithe, they give alms, and they go to synagogue. Religion is their life.' The man who spoke looked tired and resigned 'I am just an ordinary man, I have to work and I have a family. I don't have the time to be religious.'

Jesus spoke firmly 'Don't think that I am going to tell you that the religion of our fathers is wrong! Far from it, I have come to tell you that it doesn't go far enough! The old law is entirely concerned with what you do and how you do it. I tell you this; you must not be content with the mere observances of God's laws, you must write them on your hearts. You must love as God loves and then you will act has God acts.'

Another man nearby was eager to be heard. 'Most of us are poor' he said 'we need so many things. I have a family and I worry all the time about how I am going to provide for them.'

Jesus was sympathetic. 'After my father died' he said 'I too had to bring up a family so I know what is on your heart, but I have learnt that God's love is bounteous. He provides for the birds of the air and even the lilies of the field and he will provide for each one of us. Solomon in all his glory was not as fine as one of these small flowers.' Jesus bent down and picking a red anemone held it high for all to see.

'We may not become as rich in worldly goods as Solomon did but God knows what we need and if we have faith in him he will take care of us. Worrying does no good. You can't change anything by being anxious!

He smiled at the man. 'You're going a little bald on top' he said 'but does worrying about it help your hair to grow? No! Being anxious is a fruitless occupation, a waste of energy! Learn to trust God in all his goodness and you will be given everything you need.'

Jesus lifted his voice so that it reached to the edges of the crowd. 'I want you all to know about God's great love. He loves us all, sinner and righteous alike. He does not discriminate. He allows the rain to fall on all our fields.

So we must strive to be more like him. It is not for us to be judgemental of fellow beings. It is not for us to criticise. Each one of us must look to perfect his own behaviour and his relationship with God before he should dare to judge others.'

'We must learn to love each other as God loves us, only then will God's kingdom come on earth as it is in Heaven.'

There was another interruption from the crowd 'That's all very well' someone cried 'but there are those who it's very difficult to love! There are those who push us about and make our lives miserable.'

'There are' agreed Jesus. 'What I'm asking you to do is not the easy option. The way of love is hard. You must learn to love those who hate you, forgive those who wrong you. When evil is done to you, you must return it with good. In all things you must strive to love as God loves. You must strive to be perfect as God is perfect.'

He paused and looked sadly at them all. 'The way of love is the hardest way of all but it is the only way. It is the way that will lead us to God.'

***

When Jesus finished speaking the people were reluctant to leave and those who had brought relatives and friends who were sick saw their opportunity and began to push forward to be seen. Jesus turned to his disciples 'Remember Simon, how Sarah and Irena organised the people the other day?' he said 'can you try and do something similar? I managed to see so many more people when they were gently organised. Can you do it between you?'

'You promised me I would be going fishing 'said Simon with a chuckle 'Only this time it seems that you're the one that's pulled them in and it's my job to sort them!'

'I told you that you had all the qualifications I needed' agreed Jesus smiling.

CHAPTER TEN

'After the Sabbath we will leave for Jerusalem' said Jesus as they sat eating their evening meal at Simon's house. 'It will be good to go up together for the Passover.'

'Do you intend to stay in the city?' asked James 'or will we be coming back?'

'We'll be back again soon after' Jesus replied smiling. 'We'll pay our temple taxes and share our Passover meal together and I will spend some time with my brother. We will do as our law commands and then we will return to Galilee and complete our work here.'

'It will be good to see James again!' said Thomas 'By all accounts he's doing well in Jerusalem.'

'Yes!' agreed Jesus proudly 'Very soon he'll be a rabbi in his own right. I have much to learn from him.'

John looked up with a puzzled frown on his face. He looked at James 'I wonder, my respected elder brother, if I'll ever hear you say that you have much to learn from me!'

James laughed 'Jesus hasn't got a donkey for a brother as I have.'

John looked indignant and was ready to continue the brotherly insults but Simon interrupted quickly. 'If we're all going away for a few days there is much to do with the boats. Andrew, John, James if we go down to the boats first thing in the morning we can get a couple of hours in before Jesus needs us.'

'I'm sure there will be people to see early in the morning.' Jesus looked around 'If you all go to your homes tonight perhaps we could meet here at about the fourth hour.' He got up 'I need to find a place to be alone for a while.' He put his cloak around his shoulders and lifted the hood. 'Perhaps if I slip out through the courtyard I can avoid being seen.' He went to the back door 'I'll see you all in the morning.'

***

The next morning was warm and spring like. The lake glittered in the sunshine and the town was busy with people going about their day to day chores.

'You're not going to hang around, are you?' ask Irena anxiously.

Simon laughed 'the women want to get all the carpets our and beat them' he said to Jesus 'we're not really welcome around here today!'

'Let's walk along the beach to the next bay and we can talk there.' Jesus was quite agreeable to a change of routine 'It won't be too far for people who are sick to find us.'

Together they walked along the stony foreshore and around the point to the bay where Jesus had found Simon fished alone.

The signs of spring were all around them and the men felt an enormous sense of well being. Jesus was popular. They had never dreamt the people would follow him in such numbers and he had proved himself strong enough to deal with those who opposed him. The way ahead looked exciting and a strong sense of camaraderie was developing between them. On top of that the weather was glorious and the scenery beautiful.

James was bursting with questions. 'Tell us about the kingdom! When is it all going to happen?' He was excited 'You've hinted at so much. Will it be long now?'

Jesus looked the eager faces of his disciples. 'You don't have to wait' he said 'The kingdom is here among us now!'

'What do you mean?' demanded a surprised John 'How can it be here?'

'All you have to do is to turn right round and look' Jesus explained 'don't go looking forward to a time in the future or hanker after the past. If you have love in your heart the kingdom of God is here among us now. Open your eyes to love and you will see it.'

He smiled at their bewilderment. 'The Kingdom of Gold is a kingdom of love and love is both the power that holds the kingdom together and the weapon that protects it from evil.'

'Let the love of God grow in your hearts and you will bring in the Kingdom of God.' He paused and reached across to a thick bush that was growing nearby. He picked a hard pod and cracked it open to reveal minute black seeds.

'Look at these tiny seeds. They are so small they are like powder and yet when they fall to the ground and grow they have the potential to become a sturdy tree, a tree big enough to shelter the birds and give us all shade.' He smiled at them all 'So it is with the kingdom. If you allow a tiny kernel of love to grow in your hearts it will spread and grow and many will find comfort within its power.'

It was the children who found them first and, mindful of what Jesus had to say yesterday, the disciples allowed them through to Jesus. They settled happily around him. Jesus looked at James and picking up a small grubby boy and putting him on his knees he said 'Whoever humbles himself like this child, he is the greatest in the kingdom of heaven. Remember that!'

He looked around sadly 'There are people in this world who deliberately hurt children such as these. It would be better' he said and his voice became stern 'if those people had millstones fastened around their necks and they were drowned in the depth of the sea.'

The disciples were startled. They had seldom heard Jesus saying such things. They were shocked into silence. But Jesus was soon laughing with the children again and said happily to his disciples 'Children are much blessed by my Father. Whoever receives one child in my name receives me.'

The adults arrived soon, almost tumbling over in their hurry to find him. They crowded around him and pressed against him. Everyone wanted to touch him or talk to him. Soon he was completely surrounded and he found himself forced backwards towards the sea. 'Simon!' he called 'I'll be in danger of drowning soon. Can you go quickly and fetch a boat?'

Simon couldn't help chuckling and he and Andrew waded through the water to get away from the crowds and slipped off towards the quay. They were back with the boat within minutes and found Jesus and the disciples already up to their knees in water.

'Jump on board all of you' shouted Andrew throwing a rope to John 'It's safer up here!'

They all clambered on board laughing. 'Shall we sail off now?' asked Simon ready to pull up the sail.

'No!' said Jesus 'keep her steady Simon. I can talk to the people from here. They can all see me but no-one can get close enough to push me into the water! It's the ideal solution!'

'Look!' he said to them all 'Look up there on the hillside. Can you see the farmer sowing his seed? See how he takes a handful of seed and throws the seed around him as he walks.'

The crowd turned to watch the farmer.

'Watch!' said Jesus 'See how the grain is spread. Some of it falls on the path and look! The birds are already gathering to snatch it up. Some of it is falling on rocky ground and most of you will know that it will put down shallow roots for a while and produce fine green blades, but when the summer comes there will not be enough moisture and the green corn will wither and die' he paused.

'Now look' he said 'where the farmer is walking near the hedge. See how some of the grain is falling among the brambles, where it will struggle to survive and eventually be choked to death. And now' he continued 'watch how he is throwing the grain on the good soil. There the grain will take root and flourish and when harvest comes he will be able to gather the corn into his barns.'

He stood tall in the prow and the crowd turned to face him. 'Do you understand why I told that story? I have come to broadcast the word of God among you all. Now

I want you all to think' he paused 'what kind of soil will each of you turn out to be?'

Simon called from the stern 'Is that my cue?' he shouted.

Jesus laughed 'You really are catching on' he called back. 'Yes! Let's go and sit out in the middle of the lake for a while!'

The little sail caught the wind from the shore and the boat backed away. The crowd surged forward but could do nothing as the boat turned and swiftly sailed away.

Judas looked back at the crowd 'Perhaps we should have stayed' he mused.

Jesus looked at him 'it's good that your heart goes out to the poor' he said' but the poor will always be there, they will always need your help. You do not have much time with me and I need to teach you all so much.'

Nathaniel reached out and touched Jesus' arm. 'Will you explain the parable to us?'

'Yes Nathaniel I need you all to know what it will be like when you go out to preach to the people.'

'Us!' exclaimed Thomas.

'Yes! Each one of you!' Jesus spoke firmly 'A teacher has disciples to whom he passes on his teaching so that the disciples can go out in their turn and spread the teaching still further.'

He looked around at them all. 'You too will all become teachers. You will broadcast the good news of the kingdom to the world! But now' he continued 'let me tell you about those who will listen to you.'

'There will be those among your audience who will harden their hearts before you even speak. They are like the stony path, and the devil will take the word of God away from them as the birds swooped down on the grain. There will be those who are excited about what they hear but will not do anything to consolidate their initial enthusiasm and they will soon find other interests. They are the stony ground and the thorns and brambles represent those who are just too busy in this world to give time to anything to do with the next. The good news is soon choked out of their lives. And finally' he said 'the good soil represents the people who accept the word of God and live it. They will give you your harvest!'

'Teachers!' said Simon 'Most of us can only barely read. Fishermen yes! But teachers! Are you sure?'

'Simon, there is not a great deal of difference. A fisherman has to be able to read the signs. Like a good teacher he has to be patient and, when he has found the fish, like a good teacher, he has to use all his skill to catch them.'

Jesus spoke with confidence 'I chose you all with great care' he said. 'You all have a mission in life and you will not have to do or say anything that is beyond you. Remember' he added 'if God's love is in your heart nothing is impossible to any of you!'

Simon pulled the sail down and turned the boat into the light breeze. It lay there bobbing gently in the bright sun.

Jesus looked out across the sea and put his shawl over his head. One by one the disciples did the same. The only sound to be heard was the lap, lap of the water on the hull and the high pitched call of the eagle high in the azure blue sky.

***

When the boat sailed into the harbour at Capernaum a few hours later the crowds were waiting for them all. On the quay in the forefront of the crowds the disciples could see a small group of scribes and the chazzan from the synagogue.

'It looks like more trouble' said James apprehensively and a flicker of anxiety showed in his eyes.

'Don't be anxious James' said Jesus 'whatever it is we'll cope with it!'

As Jesus stepped out of the boat on to the quay the chazzan stepped forward and sank to his knees at Jesus' feet.

'Master' he pleaded 'My daughter is very sick. She is only twelve and I'm afraid she will die. Please come quickly and see her.'

Jesus reached down and took the man's hands and pulled him to his feet 'You don't need to kneel to me Jairus' he said 'of course I will come!'

Tears of relief welled up in Jairus' eyes. 'Come!' he said 'We must be quick!'

The scribes accompanying Jairus exchanged glances but joined with the crowd as it surged after the two men. Seeing Jesus engulfed by people Simon called to the disciples 'Andrew moor the boat. The rest of you come with me. Come on! We must stay with him. He'll need our help!'

As they hurried through the narrow streets of Capernaum towards Jairus' house the people jostled and scrambled over the cobbles. Suddenly Jesus stopped. He looked around at the people near him. 'Who touched me?' he demanded.

Simon was surprised 'Look at these crowds. They are all pushing. It could have been any of them.'

'Somebody did touch me' he said firmly. He looked around again 'I felt power go out of me!'

Despite Jairus' urgent tugging at his arm Jesus stood his ground.

A moment passed and then a woman stepped forward. She looked up at Jesus 'It was me!' she said. 'For twelve years I have had to suffer continual bleeding. No doctor has been able to help me. For twelve years I have been unclean.'

She gazed into Jesus' eyes. 'I knew' she said 'that if I could just touch your robe I would be healed.' And she looked defiantly around at all the crowd 'And I am!' her elation obvious to all.

Jesus reached out to her with a smile. He put his hand on her arm. 'Daughter' he said 'your faith has made you well. Go in peace and be content.'

He turned back to continue his journey but as he did so a servant arrived and went straight to Jairus. 'Your daughter is dead' he said to Jairus. 'Do not trouble the teacher any more.'

Jairus' face crumpled in grief and Jesus went straight to his side and said quietly in his ear 'Do not fear' he said 'only believe and she will be well.'

They heard the wailing before they reached the house and as they turned the corner they saw the women of the town gathered on the steps in front of the house. Dressed in black they rocked and wailed and poured handfuls of ash over their heads.

When Jesus arrived, Jairus' wife rushed out to meet him her face running with tears.

'Don't be afraid' he said 'She is not dead. She is only sleeping!'

The mourners stopped their wailing. 'Of course she's dead' they scoffed 'What does a young man like you know about death?'

Jesus turned to the disciples 'Keep the crowds back' he ordered. 'Simon, James, John come with me' and he went with the parents into the room where the child lay.

From the noise and bustle of the street the silence in the little room made the parents' grief all the more poignant.

The little girl lay on the bed. He limbs had already been straightened and her hair brushed. He parents clung to each other and rocked silently.

Jesus stepped into the room and nodded to John to close the door behind them. He walked over to the bed where the child lay and bending over her he gently took both her hands in his. 'Little lamb' he said quietly as though not wanting to startle her 'it's time to get up!'

The little girl opened her eyes and looking up at Jesus she smiled and began to sit up.

Her parents gasped in shock and relief and Jesus turned to them 'She's perfectly well now and I think she may even be hungry.' He looked enquiringly at the child.

She nodded and with a laugh she scrambled off the bed and into her father's arms.

'Give her something to eat!' said Jesus and then he looked at the disciples and the parents. 'Tell no-one what has happened here today. It will be too much for people to understand.'

'And for us!' whispered John to his brother.

The bewildered mourners were given their money and sent away and before long the rumours were rife.

'I think it's just as well we're leaving for Jerusalem in a couple of days' Jesus confided in Simon 'the speculation and rumours may be over by the time we get back.'

Simon raised his eyebrows and Jesus laughed 'You think that's wishful thinking? Oh well!'

CHAPTER ELEVEN

Jesus disappeared for three days. Only Irena seemed to know where he might be but all she said was 'You boys get yourselves ready to go to Jerusalem and he'll be back when the Sabbath is over.'

On the morning of the first day of the week when they woke and gathered at Simon's house they found Jesus sitting in the morning sun looking out at the sea. He looked refreshed and eager to get going.

Other men from Capernaum were going to make the annual pilgrimage and there was definitely a holiday feel in the air as they all greeted each other on the road. Everyone carried a bed roll and a small bag of food.

The women stood in the doorway of their houses and looked out at the groups of men with affection and pride. For over a week the women would take care of the houses and businesses. Only the sick and elderly men had been left behind, along with a few who had been excused by the rabbi. A newly married man could stay. A man who had recently bought oxen that needed breaking in or a man who had bought new land that he had not yet planted, these too could be excused.

But most men looked forward all year to their week away in Jerusalem. They had made this trip all their lives. It was their annual holiday.

As Jesus and the disciples strode out along the road small groups of men from the hill villages joined the others where their paths met the lake road. At the junction with Tiberias the men from Nazareth joined the main party. Judas, Joses and Simon were among them and so were the young men who had disturbed the synagogue service. They looked shame faced when they saw Jesus, especially when he went over to speak with them. He greeted them affably and enquired after their families. They had known Jesus all their lives. What they had done surprised even them but Jesus was treating them as if it had never happened. Their relief soon turned to laughter and soon all the men were in high spirits as they walked towards Beth Shan and the Jordan valley beyond.

It would have been shorter to cut through the Samarian hills and enter Jerusalem from the north but instead the large crowd of Galileans chose to take the Jordan valley route to Jericho and then climb out of the valley and enter Jerusalem from the East.

Years of experience had taught them that the Samaritans resented Jewish pilgrims using their province as a corridor to Jerusalem. Just the sight of so many men walking together was enough to provoke Samaritan youths to stone throwing and abuse. It was better to journey together in peace. At least in the Jordan valley it was warm enough for them not to need to find rooms. A bed roll around a camp fire only added to the sense of adventure and holiday.

Without pushing too hard the journey usually took three days with one stop at the top of the valley and the second at Jericho.

Jericho played host to the pilgrims from Galilee every year. Even if they had travelled through Samaria many men would go down to Jericho just to experience the ascent to Jerusalem in the company of friends.

Climbing out of the valley behind Jericho before the sun came up, the pilgrims were able to complete the hardest part of their journey while it was still cool.

After a breakfast of bread and figs the singing started. A large number of cantors were scattered among the men and as they walked with the rising sun on their backs the men lifted their voices and their spirits and sang to the Lord.

Every year they sang the psalms, leaving the last special psalms until they reached the road that climbed the Mount of Olives. Most of them knew the psalms by heart but with the cantors leading them the men only had to join in with the refrains if they couldn't remember all the words.

Excitement mounted as they walked. The anticipation of seeing Jerusalem as the sun set behind the golden face of Herod's new building made the long journey worthwhile.

Standing on the Mount of Olives at last Jesus and his disciples joined with all the men to sing

'Praise the Lord!

For it is good to sing praises to our God:

For He is gracious, and a song of praise is seemly.'

And then together the pilgrims, still singing, walked down to the Kidron valley and up through the Golden Gate into the Temple itself. 'Praise God in his sanctuary' they sang.

It was their custom to pay their annual temple tax as soon as they arrived and then to go back to their camping grounds on the slopes of the Mount of Olives.

This year they arrived well before the tax booths closed and it was with relief that they left the darkening courts and retraced their steps to the olive gardens on the mount where they could rest. Small groups of Roman soldiers hovered around the main gates of the Temple and several passed on horseback as they made their way up the Kidron Valley path back to their barracks in the Tower of Antonio.

Not used to such a show of authority the Galilean pilgrims eyed them nervously and hurriedly returned to set up camps in the high walled gardens on the mount.

Judas was particularly irate about the Roman presence. His hand kept straying to his waist where once he had kept his dagger and it was Matthew that calmed him down. 'Let them patrol the streets and keep the peace. It's hard, thankless work and they hate it' he said in his steady measure tone. 'If they are doing it we Jews don't have to. Think of them as our servants. It will make you feel better.'

Judas shrugged 'Their days are numbered anyway!' he muttered darkly.

'I daresay they are' agreed Matthew with a smile 'Civilisations come and go. It's bound to be their turn soon!'

Behind the security of the garden wall it wasn't long before they all relaxed around the camp fire. As darkness fell, the city lights flickered and gleamed through the branches of the olive trees. The camaraderie of the moment felt good.

They didn't notice the stranger until he was right there among them. He stood there in the shadows watching them for a moment and then he stepped forward into the fire light.

Jesus saw him first.

'James!' he exclaimed jumping to his feet 'It's so good to see you brother!'

The two men embraced and then, as the men shuffled to make room, they sat down together in the circle.

'I knew exactly when and where to find you' said James happily 'same time, same place, every year!'

'Hello James!' called John with a broad grin 'Your brother says he has a lot to learn from you. It looks like it's going to be a long night!'

'Little cousin!' replied James peering into the darkness 'You seem to have grown!'

'Your beard has too!' retorted John 'You look very distinguished.'

'I have to look the part' James laughed 'Everybody here in Jerusalem is so clever, the beard gives me confidence.'

'You're clever enough!' said Jesus 'How have you been? You look well!'

'I am' agreed James 'But it's a punishing schedule. Rabbi Gamaliel insists on his students being ready for class on the dot of the first hour. Mind you' he continued 'I'm glad to be with him. He really is the best!'

'I'm glad you're with him too' said Jesus 'He is a man of great compassion and what he teaches always come from the heart.'

'He is a good man' agreed James 'It's such a shame that other teachers don't take a leaf out of his book. Do you know?' he laughed 'the latest important theological discussion that is taxing the great minds at the moment is the question about a woman whose husband dies and so she becomes the wife of his brother who in his turn dies and she becomes the next brother's wife. In the end seven brothers die and so does the woman. Now the question that is causing so much discussion is whose wife will she be in the after life?' He looked at Jesus 'Can you imagine it?' he laughed again 'It's such a far fetched scenario that it is ridiculous to make it such an issue!'

'It is' agreed Jesus 'But even the silliest of questions should be answered if it is possible.'

'Is it possible?' asked James.

'The truth is' replied Jesus 'that in the Kingdom of Heaven the formalities we think so much of here on earth don't exist at all. Why would a marriage licence be needed in heaven? The only bonds in heaven are the bonds of love. Each man or woman is a person in their own right, they don't belong to someone else, but they can love and be loved. Each person is whole and uniquely special in the eyes of God.' Jesus smiled 'Uniquely special and much loved!'

'I'll try dropping that into tomorrow's debate' said James getting to his feet. 'I'll say that the great rabbi Jesus of Nazareth says that the scholars of Jerusalem are all wasting valuable time discussing such a trivial matter! But right now' he said pulling his cloak around him 'it's bed for me. I'd stay and keep you company but I've got a nice soft bed waiting for me! I'll see you tomorrow. Sleep well!'

The shadows swallowed him before he had finished speaking and his departure had everyone stretching and yawning and thinking of bed. Their eyes closed the moment their heads touched the ground.

***

The following morning they slept on as the sun rose over the top of the hill and were still bleary eyed when the noise of passing pilgrims on the nearby track startled them awake.

Only two full days remained before the Passover celebrations began and once awake they organised themselves swiftly. They needed to go to the Temple and purchase lambs for sacrifice and they needed to find somewhere within the city walls to have their Passover meal together.

'I meant to ask James if we could use his room or if Gamaliel would allow us a room in his house' said Jesus 'but his unexpected visit last night took me by surprise. I'll make a point of finding him today' he continued 'and get something organised.'

Everybody had very soon rolled up their beds and tucked them in the branches of the trees and, leaving the high walled garden, they joined the pilgrims making for the Golden Gate.

Inside the gate the noise and the hustle and bustle took them by surprise. When they had entered last night people had already left for their homes and the stalls were closing down, but now, in the morning sun, the temple courts teemed with excited men and women eager to go about their business and see the sights.

The disciples were no different and looked excitedly around. The gold plates on the eastern front of the Temple

103

itself caught the sun and made the huge building gleam its welcome. The rest of the temple buildings showed clean white blocks of limestone and workmen were still working on the portico facades.

Thomas and Jesus' brothers were fascinated by the building itself. The size of the stones caused them to stop in amazement. Even in Sepphoris the building was never on this scale. They watched the workmen on the porticoes. How had they managed to move such enormous stones?

They moved across the open courtyard to the northern entrance through which shepherds could be seen waiting patiently with their flocks. Temple officials were giving receipts and then allowing lambs to be herded into small pens. The bleating of sheep separated from their young and the piteous cries of the lambs filled the air.

To buy a lamb for sacrifice was essential and soon the men were carrying their chosen lambs back across the court towards the central gateway that led into the Court of Women and then up more steps to the Court of Israel. Here they waited patiently in the long queue.

Finely dressed priests with their servants bustled around and the air was thick with the smell of smoke and roasting and boiling flesh. Blood ran freely from the altar in front of the Temple entrance and the servants constantly sluiced it away into drains cut in the limestone.

As the pilgrims reached the head of the queue the receipt they had received when paying their tax was checked, as was the receipt they had just received when buying their lamb. Any poor man coming in from the country and bringing his own lamb was immediately pounced upon and a defect in the lamb was instantly discovered. Dispatched to buy another lamb from the official pens the man would be forced to queue all over again while his own lamb was confiscated and sent round to the official pens to be bought by someone else.

It had always been this way. Every Passover week a million or so pilgrims in Jerusalem financed the running of the Temple for a whole year.

The priests' salaries depended upon this week. It would be a disaster if anything happened to disturb the tradition.

The sacrifice completed, a small portion of the lamb was given to each pilgrim to be consumed at their own Passover meal. Wrapping the meat in a cloth the pilgrims were then free to do as they pleased. Their official duties were done.

When Jesus and his brothers left the Temple they went to look for James and waited in the shade of a cypress tree in the courtyard of Gamaliel's house until his class finished.

'I've arranged for us to have our Passover meal at Uncle Joseph's house' he said 'Give me the meat and I'll give it to the servants. You don't want to carry that around with you for two days!'

'I haven't seen Uncle Joseph for years' said Joses 'this is great news. His house is so big!'

'He's often abroad as you know' agreed James 'but he's getting much older now and doesn't travel so much. He's been very good to me while I've been here.'

'He says to tell you' James continued 'not to bother about the meal. His house is big enough for you all, including all your disciples Jesus, and he's rich enough to pay for the food.' He grinned at his brothers. 'Now you can just be tourists, while I go back to study!'

He turned to return into the house and then suddenly stopped 'Jesus! Joseph also said I should warn you that news of what you have been doing in Galilee has reached the ears of the religious leaders here. He advises you to be cautious.'

He paused and looked Jesus in the eyes 'Be careful brother!' he said 'You don't want it all to end before it has a chance to start.'

CHAPTER TWELVE

Many of the disciples had relatives in Jerusalem and the others just revelled in the sights and sounds of the city. They all met up on the steps of the Bethesda pool. Just outside the city walls by the Sheep Gate the steps were a popular place to sit and wait. The Tower of Antonia loomed over the area and cast a shadow over the pool in the middle of the day but that made waiting on the steps all the more pleasant.

Jesus and his brothers arrived in the mid afternoon to find that most of the others had arrived. Judas was the only one missing but he was known to have many friends to visit.

They all sat companionably in the warm afternoon sun and watched people coming and going. There were a larger number than usual of the sick and infirm who accompanied by a relative or friend, lay on the steps in the hope that the water of the pool would begin to shudder. It was thought that the water was disturbed by an angel from God and that the first person to get into the water after it was disturbed would be healed of their infirmity.

So the sick waited in hope and pilgrims using the steps as a meeting place salved their consciences by giving alms before going on to the Temple.

As they waited for Judas to arrive Jesus talked quietly to a man lying on a mattress nearby. He had been ill nearly all of his life and was unable to walk on his own.

'I've been ill for thirty years' he told Jesus with a voice full of self pity and just a touch of pride.

Jesus looked at him sternly. 'Do you want to get well?' he asked.

'Of course I do!' the man was indignant 'but when the water is disturbed I have no one to help me down into the water. Someone always gets there before me.'

Jesus looked at him long and hard 'Get up!' he ordered. 'Get up! Roll up your bed and walk.'

The man was bemused. 'I can't!' he said plaintively.

'Yes you can!' said Jesus 'Stand up!'

Gingerly the man pushed down on his hands and felt the strength surge through his body. He hadn't walked for so long that when he stood upright he tottered a little and then stood straight.

'See!' said Jesus with a smile 'You are well!'

Picking up his bed his eyes round with amazement the man bounded away. He didn't even ask Jesus who he was.

Later, when he was asked, he took people back to look for the miracle worker, but when he reached Bethesda Jesus had gone.

'I would like to visit my old friend Lazarus in Bethany' Jesus said to them all when Judas had joined them. 'You will all be welcome.'

It was a short walk across the Kidron valley and up the Mount of Olives and there was no doubt about the welcome when they arrived at the little white house. Perched on the hill on the edge of the village with a courtyard covered with vines the view down over the Judean desert was spectacular.

A quiet, slim young man, Lazarus was delighted to see Jesus and his friends. Servants appeared from nowhere and the men's feet were washed and cold drinks were served. His two sisters took their cloaks and spoke to each of the men making sure they all felt included, but it was Jesus they obviously adored.

The house was cool and they all sat gratefully on the cushions. It was good to feel the thick carpets beneath their bare feet.

Lazarus was eager to hear the news. 'There have been rumours already about what you are doing in Galilee' he said excitedly 'Is this the beginning? Has the time come at last?'

Jesus smiled at him 'Yes Lazarus it has!' he replied.

'Will you be staying here in Jerusalem now?' Lazarus asked 'You can all stay here. We'll find the room somehow!'

'No! I'm not ready for Jerusalem yet' Jesus was serious. 'I have to live and teach the kingdom first so that my friends here can continue when I'm gone.'

Mary, Lazarus' younger sister was entering the room with a plate of food. She put it down hurriedly and ran over to Jesus. 'Don't talk like that!' she cried 'It sounds as if you expect something to happen to you. I can't bear it!'

Jesus took her hands. 'It will all be well Mary' he said 'I have a lot to do first. You must not worry.'

Still clutching at Jesus' hands Mary sank down on to the carpet at his feet. There were tears in her eyes.

Jesus turned back to Lazarus. 'I do believe I have chosen the hardest of ways' he said 'God has given me his power but I can only use it for love. It's been strange to discover how resistant people are to love.'

'It's because love has a way of showing up our inadequacies' said Simon. 'I should know!'

'But love also has a way of caring so much for the person that inadequacies are forgiven and forgotten' Jesus replied.

Matthew looked up '"Though your sins be as scarlet, yet shall they become as white as snow"' said the Lord. Or' he smiled 'so says the prophet Isaiah.'

'There is nothing as powerful as the love of God. And yet there is nothing as obstinate as the hearts of man!' Jesus looked sad.

A clatter of pans from the kitchen broke the silence that followed and Martha bustled indignantly into the room. 'I need Mary to help! There are so many of you to feed, I can't do it alone. Jesus you tell her.'

Jesus got up from the cushions immediately and went over to the hot and flustered woman taking her in his arms. 'Martha' he said kindly 'You have the worries and cares of the world on your shoulders. You don't need to get so stressed. You must not allow yourself to be worried by so many things.'

He stood back and looked into her face. 'There is only one thing that is important and Mary has chosen it. Let her stay!'

'I'm sorry Jesus' Martha flushed with embarrassment 'I get so tired and it makes me upset.'

'All the more reason for you to sit down as well' Jesus took her hand and led her to the cushions. She sank down gratefully but still with an anxious frown.

Jesus passed her his drink 'Come on Martha, relax for a while and then we'll all help you in the kitchen.'

That made her laugh! 'Jesus!' she exclaimed 'I've heard they're calling you a miracle worker but you and your friends cooking? That's a bit too much to take!'

'I'll have you know that my mother in law says I'm pretty good at cooking fish' protested Simon.

'There's no fish in the house!' said Martha thankfully, making them all laugh.

***

After the meal they all walked down to the Garden of Gethsemane and finding their bed rolls just as they left them they didn't attempt to light a fire. With a warm meal inside them they felt contented and at peace. It wasn't long before they were asleep.

Nobody noticed when Jesus got up and went away into the shadows to pray.

***

The following day Jesus spent in the Temple. In the Court of the Women the teachers sat in the shade of the porticoes with their disciples at their feet. Anyone could stand on the edge of such a group and listen to the discussions and join in if invited to do so.

Jesus' demeanour marked him out as a man of authority and the rabbis didn't hesitate to ask him to speak. Remembering Joseph's message Jesus was careful not to say too much but it wasn't long before people were asking 'Who is that man?'

Even the teachers found themselves asking his advice. Here was a man who spoke with authority. It was certainly refreshing.

The day passed without event but the Temple elders and officials curious about Jesus were beginning to hover and ask questions and it was a relief to Simon when the horns sounded as the sun went below the horizon and everyone began to leave the Temple.

The next morning heralded a day of sacrifices. Lambs were slaughtered and the altar fires burnt throughout the day. All the official Temple sacrifices were saved for this, the last day before the high Sabbath.

The stalls and shops in the outer court and in the city were busy as people rushed around buying food enough to cope with their extra guests. It was not only the Temple coffers that were filling this week.

That evening the men went to the Temple to welcome the Sabbath. The sun was a brilliant red orb as it sank behind the western hills and the sound of several thousand men's voices, as they sang the hymn of welcome, made chests burst with pride and eyes fill with tears. The roof tops were still tinged with red and the music still sang in their hearts as Jesus and his young companions climbed up to old Joseph's house for their Passover meal.

It was as Joses had remembered, a lovely old house, large and graceful with beautifully tiled floors and spacious rooms. Every room opened out on to a balcony or courtyard from which a person could stand and look down over the city.

Joseph himself greeted them at the door. An elderly man now, with greying hair, there was no mistaking that here was a man who was used to being in control. A kinsman of Jesus' mother and a much travelled merchant, he had an air of confidence that you seldom found in his compatriots.

He was delighted to see his nephews and their friends 'It makes me feel young again to be sitting around a table with you youngsters' he said happily.

John, as the youngest male present, was required to start the proceeding by asking the question 'Why is this night different from all other nights?' and Joseph solemnly replied

'Because we were Pharaoh's slaves in Egypt, the Lord our God brought us out from there with a mighty hand and an outstretched arm and if the Most Holy, blessed be he, had not brought out our ancestors from Egypt, we and our children and our children's children would still be in bondage to the pharaohs in Egypt.'

And then the lamps on the table were lit and the wine glasses filled and the meal commenced.

Every year the ceremony was the same and the young men remembered Passover meals at home with their families and thought about those they loved. Not many of them had experienced the luxury they shared this night.

A couple of Joseph's friends were with them for the meal. One of them, an elderly Pharisee named Nicodemus, asked Jesus to join him out on the balcony when the meal was over. The two men stood together and looked down on the flickering lights of the city.

The old man turned to Jesus and his face was troubled 'I have heard of all the things you have been doing in Galilee' he said 'I knew when I had the news that it was impossible for you to do these things unless God was with you. Now I have met you I feel certain I am right. Tell me' he implored 'what must I do to find salvation?'

Jesus' reply was uncompromising and when he turned to face the old man his eyes were still and serious. 'It is necessary for all people to be born again in order to enter the kingdom.'

'What do you mean "born again"? How can someone who is old enter the womb and be born again?'

Jesus answered 'It is not the birth of the flesh that I am talking about but the birth of the Spirit. To be born of the Spirit means a new life in which the Spirit of God takes over and leads you into new and exciting ways.'

Nicodemus sounded puzzled 'But how can these things happen?' he asked.

Jesus smiled at him 'Don't tell me that the great teacher Nicodemus doesn't understand what I'm talking about!'

Nicodemus shrugged and Jesus went on 'If you believe in the things I have done then you have it in you to believe that I have come from God and will one day return to him.'

He paused 'Open your heart Nicodemus and allow the Spirit of God to enter!'

Nicodemus sighed 'I am an old man and what you have challenged me to do is new and very frightening. What if the Spirit of God takes over my life and leads me to where I don't want to go?'

It was Jesus' turn to be sad 'Yes' he agreed 'It could certainly happen that way1'

He put his hand out to touch Nicodemus' arm 'But God is compassionate and all we can do is to put ourselves in his hands and trust in his mercy.'

Nicodemus did not reply. He stood gazing down at the city. The Temple buildings glowed with the light of the torches on its walls. He had grown up in this city, studied the scriptures and taught in the Temple courts and now when he should be contemplating a distinguished retirement he was being challenged to start again. Challenged by a young man, a descendant of the great King David through his father's line and from Aaron the priest through his mother. King and Priest, the Anointed One. Tears welled in his eyes. There was no doubt in his heart. Here was the expected one. If only he was young again. What possible use could God have for an old man like him?

CHAPTER THIRTEEN

Deciding to return to Galilee by walking through the uplands of Samaria Jesus and his small group found that, by taking this route, the journey was easier and the air cooler. Along the road small groups of men huddled together and muttered as they passed and occasionally a door was slammed in anger, but they didn't experience any serious trouble. They travelled several miles before midday and reaching the well outside the town of Sychar they thankfully sat for a few minutes.

'I'll go in to the town and buy some food' offered Judas.

'Don't go alone' said Matthew 'it might not be safe!'

'Why don't you all go?' asked Jesus 'I'll stay here in the shade of this tree and we can all eat together when you get back.'

The disciples did not protest. They had become accustomed to Jesus' desire to be alone at times and soon set off together towards the town.

Left alone Jesus leant back against the tree trunk and gazed after them.

The women generally used the wells in the morning and the evening when the air was cool. Then they would come chattering and colourful, like a flock of forest birds, to fill their water jars and catch up on the local gossip.

At midday with the heat of the sun baking the earth the well was deserted. Jesus closed his eyes.

He opened them again when a noise disturbed him. There, at the mouth of the well was a single woman lowering a bucket down the stone lined sides. She lowered it three times before her jar was filled and then Jesus spoke. 'Will you give me a little water to drink?' he asked.

She jerked around startled, her face coloured with indignation and surprise. 'Oh!' she said disdainfully 'You can speak then? I thought it would be beneath you, a Jew, to speak to me, a Samaritan!'

Jesus smiled 'I would be glad of a little water' he said.

She pursed her lips and bent to dip an old cup into the water. 'Here you are!' she said as she shoved the cup towards him.

Jesus bowed his head in thanks and took the cup from her hand. Then he drank and gave her back the cup and looking into her eyes he said 'I have asked you for water and you have given me clear, cold water to refresh me. If now you in your turn ask me for water I, in the power of God, will give you living water.'

The woman looked puzzled 'Sir' she said 'The well is deep and you have nothing to draw with. Where will you get that living water?' She was scornful 'Are you setting yourself up to be more important than our ancestor Jacob who founded this place and gave us this well?'

Jesus spoke slowly, allowing his words to pierce the armour of scorn. 'Every one who drinks of the water from this well will thirst again but whoever drinks of the water that I shall give will never thirst; the water that I shall give will become in him a spring of water welling up to eternal life.'

The woman was silenced. This was no ordinary Jewish traveller. She had made a mistake being so contemptuous.

And yet this man had obviously taken no offence and he was talking to her as though she was an equal. Obviously he didn't know anything about her otherwise he'd be like any other 'holier than thou' man.

Deciding to keep her response light hearted, she smiled 'Sir, give me some of this water. Then I need never thirst again nor indeed come to this well and carry water every day.'

Jesus looked at her 'First' he said 'Go and fetch your husband!'

'I don't have a husband!' she snapped.

'I know!' Jesus replied slowly 'Instead you have had five lovers and are living with one of them now. That is why you come to the well alone in the middle of the day. That way you can avoid the other women and their gossip.'

The woman was shocked. She stared at Jesus in horror. 'Who are you? How do you know these things?' Her cheeks had become flushed with embarrassment. 'Are you a prophet?'

Jesus looked at her calmly.

Growing ever more flustered she tried to change the subject 'If you are a prophet tell me this. You Jews go to Jerusalem to worship and we Samaritans worship God here on Mt Gerizim. Who is right?'

Jesus smiled at her confusion. 'The time is coming when such a question will not be important' he said 'God does not dwell in Temples. God is Spirit and can be worshipped anywhere by true worshippers who have the Spirit of love in their hearts.'

'I know when the Messiah comes things will be different!' she continued to argue.

Jesus stopped her with a look 'That moment has come' he said 'I am he.'

The woman's face crumpled and Jesus reached up and touched her hands. 'You are trying to build a wall to protect yourself from the scorn of others. That makes you aggressive. But underneath' Jesus continued with sadness in his eyes 'you hate your life and feel ashamed.'

The woman started to weep.

Jesus continued 'Go now and put your life in order. Open your heart to God and you will indeed be filled with living water and your life will be saved.'

The disciples arrived back to se Jesus talking with the woman. They didn't interrupt and stood back until the woman ran off. She ran to the town 'Come and see' she called to everyone 'there is a prophet at the well who I think is the Messiah.' In her excitement she left her water jar behind.

As they sat down to share the food Jesus got up to walk away. They were all anxious and urged him to eat but Jesus seemed to be fired with a new energy. 'I have food to eat' he said 'My food is to do the will of God and to complete his work.'

'In Jerusalem' he went on 'I was quiet. The time to challenge had not yet come. There is still much ground work to be done. Now I need to work without stopping and I need your help.'

He paused 'The teaching must go on until the whole of mankind has heard of God's love. I sow and you will reap. In your turn you will sow and others will reap, until that day when God's Kingdom comes.'

He stood looking down towards the town. People were hurrying out of their houses and running out to see if what the woman had said was true. She had sown the seed.

Jesus' heart was filled with compassion 'Lift up your eyes' he said to the disciples 'the fields are already white for harvest.'

***

They stayed at Sychar for two days. The people of the town gave them accommodation and food and crowded to hear Jesus speak. They brought their sick for him to heal and when Jesus was ready to move on they were sad. They turned to the woman 'You were right' they agreed 'we have seen for ourselves and, like you, we believe him to be the Messiah.'

As they were leaving the uplands, and the great fertile Plain of Esdraelon lay before them, a group of men stood across the path. As Jesus and his disciples approached they began to call out 'Jesus! Jesus! Have mercy on us!'

'They're lepers!' whispered the younger Simon to James.

'Don't worry' replied James 'you'll be quite safe. Just watch!'

Jesus continued to walk forwards towards the lepers with the disciples following more slowly. As they got nearer some of the lepers had dropped to their knees 'Help us master' they pleaded.

'Stand up!' ordered Jesus 'Stand tall all of you! Go now and show yourselves to the priests.'

They stood bemused. 'Heal us. Touch us and heal us!' they were desperate.

'It is not necessary' replied Jesus 'Just go!'

The lepers turned and reluctantly walked back along the road. Then as they walked they noticed their skin beginning to change. They stopped to stare at each other in wonderment and watched as skin became new once more. Then in excitement and whooping for joy they turned again and ran.

The disciples laughed with them. They could empathise with the leper's relief. Now they could return to their families.

Jesus stood still in the middle of the path and watched the retreating men. Suddenly one of them stopped and looking back at Jesus he turned and ran back. When he reached Jesus he fell on his face in front of him. 'Thank you master' he said 'Thank you and may God be praised!'

Jesus looked down at him 'Out of the group of ten men, only one of you has the grace to return to say thank you and,' he said slowly 'and you are a Samaritan!'

'Yes master I am!' the man agreed, lifting his head to look at Jesus.

Jesus leant down and gave the man his hand. 'Get up!' he said 'Go on your way. Your faith has saved you!'

As the man ran on to join his fellows Jesus turned to his disciples. 'When we are in distress it comes easily to us to beg for God's help. If we could remember to say thank you for all the help we receive it would make the heart of God very glad indeed.'

***

Crossing the plain they reached the Roman road which, coming up from the coast, skirted the Galilean hills and led up the Western shore of the Sea of Galilee, on to Capernaum and then on still further to Damascus.

It was a well travelled road and when they reached it Jesus' brothers left the road almost immediately and climbed the hill to Nazareth.

Jesus and his disciples continued along the road until, as evening came, they reached Magdala. Only three more miles to go!

The sun had already gone down behind the hills and the village was in shadow but as they looked out across the lake the eastern hills were glowing pink as the rays of the sun caught them in its dying throes.

It felt good to be near home and they began to quicken their pace.

Magdala seemed busy. Several people were out on the road or standing in the doorways of their homes. They greeted Jesus and his disciples with a sense of suppressed excitement. As they walked they heard people whispering 'He's back!' and children wriggled out between the adults in the doorways and ran out to Jesus grabbing his hands and clutching on to his robes.

They reached the house on the edge of the village and a man stepped out to greet him. 'Jesus!' he said 'Come into my house. You and your disciples, and have a meal before you go on your way.'

Jesus hesitated 'Good evening Simon' he said 'but we are nearly home'. And glancing at Simon and Andrew he continued 'We will be expected soon.'

'Nevertheless you will come in now, won't you?' the man was insistent. 'I have wanted to speak to you about your work.'

Jesus was gracious 'We would be pleased to come in for a while' he said and followed Simon as he led the way into the house. Those on the street followed behind and stood in the doorway of a spacious room where Simon indicated that they should sit on the cushions around a low table. He clapped his hands and servants appeared with dishes of food which they placed in front of them all.

Simon was a Pharisee. The food was adequate but not rich in sauces and the furniture and decoration comfortable but sparse. He wasted no time and began straight away to ask Jesus questions. Where had Jesus studied? What were his opinions about the Sabbath day regulations? What did he think about the Messianic prophesies?

Jesus answered his questions politely. He looked tired and he did not have time to eat but his disciples did so thankfully. There was no wine to drink but clear, cold water was served by the servants.

Simon was a man who expected to be looked up to. He was educated and pious and the people of Magdala stood in awe of him. He was so involved with his academic discussion with Jesus that he did not notice that his guest had not yet managed to put food in his mouth.

'And the after life? What do you think of the argument between the Pharisaic party and the Sadducees?' he urged Jesus again for an answer.

Jesus sighed and shook his head to dispel his tiredness. With a small cry of distress a woman who was standing in the doorway ran in to the room and knelt beside Jesus. Crying bitterly now, she took out a vial of sweet smelling ointment and began to pour some on to his bare feet. Her tears mingled with the ointment and she hurriedly wiped his feet with her long hair.

Simon was horrified by this intrusion. He stared at Jesus in disbelief. 'Are you really some kind of a prophet?' he demanded 'Surely if you were you would know that this woman is a prostitute. What she is doing is unforgivable!' He glared down at the woman 'What are you doing in my house? Everything about you is unclean! Get out!'

The woman began to struggle to her feet but Jesus put out a hand and touched her arm. 'Stay' he said quietly and turned to the Pharisee.

'Simon' he said 'I have something to say to you.' The room was suddenly silent. All eyes were on the two men. Jesus continued 'Two men owed money to a creditor; one owed a hundred denarii, the other fifty. When the time came to pay neither could so the creditor forgave them both. Which man do you think would be most grateful and love the creditor most?' He looked at Simon.

Simon answered 'The one who was forgiven most I suppose' he said reluctantly.

Jesus stood and looked down at the woman. 'You see this woman Simon? I came into your house as your guest and you gave me no water to wash my feet or oil to anoint my head. But this woman has washed my feet with her tears and anointed my feet with ointment.'

He looked directly into Simon's eyes. 'She has shown much love and her sins, which are many, are all forgiven. As a result her love will grow still more.'

He reached down to the woman taking her hand and helping her to her feet. 'Your sins are indeed forgiven. Your faith has saved you. Go in peace!'

Simon was startled and looked at Jesus angrily 'Who do you think you are?' he exclaimed 'It's not up to you to forgive sins.'

Jesus stood tall 'We are tired and need to finish our journey.' He inclined his head towards his host. 'Thank you Simon for inviting us into you house.' Pausing for a moment he then continued 'Remember' he said 'Love is the key to the Kingdom. It is more important than theology, than religion, than laws. Be wary for your own soul Simon, and be careful not to think yourself so perfect that you believe you do not need God's forgiveness and his love.'

With that Jesus turned and walked from the room and the disciples scrambled to their feet and followed.

Outside in the street the woman watched as Jesus waked away. Pushing back her long, red hair a look of determination came over her face and then she, too, hurried away and disappeared into the shadows.

CHAPTER FOURTEEN

She was there the next morning when they woke. They found her with Irena and the two women were talking quietly together as they prepared the morning food. She looked up as Jesus entered the room 'I had to come!' she said defiantly.

'I knew you would' Jesus concurred 'You don't have to be afraid. I'm not going to send you away.'

Irena turned to Jesus 'Mary has been telling me how you were treated last night' she said indignantly, and she put down the bowl she was carrying and wiped her hands.

'We have a plan!'

Simon, entering the room with Sarah by his side, rolled his eyes to heaven. 'May God preserve us!' he muttered.

'Without our help' retorted Irena 'he will be hard pressed to do so!' She glared at her son-in-law who gave a happy chuckle and kissed his wife with adoring eyes.

'Tell us about your plan Irena' said Jesus smiling.

Irena glanced at Mary. 'Every time you leave Capernaum you take the boys further and further a field' she said 'and it will get worse!'

'Mary and I propose that I make up a rota of women who want to help and when you journey there will always be two of us with you to look after your food and your clothes. It will be our job to see that you and the boys are well fed.'

'Already' she added 'Joanna, Chuza's wife, has offered both her time and her money to help you. So has Susanna and Salome and James and John's mother has offered her help too.'

Mary interrupted 'Irena must stay here but I too can help!' she pleaded.

Jesus smiled. 'Yes Mary you can. God has an important role for you to play.'

'How can that be?' she was taken aback. 'I am nothing but a sinner!'

'No Mary!' said Jesus firmly, 'You were a sinner. Now you are forgiven! Your slate has been wiped clean! God definitely has a mission for you and what you did for me last night will never be forgotten.'

Mary blushed and Irena touched her arm. 'He's right' she said 'We need you. Help me to get the women organised and between us we can look after both Jesus and our men!'

'Of course I will help' agreed Mary 'it makes my heart feel good to know that, after many years of being rejected, I am at last wanted.'

She looked at Jesus with love in her eyes 'I will stay with you to the very end' she said.

Jesus returned her gaze. 'Thank you Mary' he replied 'It will make my heart glad to know you are there.'

Andrew bustled into the room. 'Jesus!' he said 'the crowd outside is already beginning to grow. Can you come out to them yet?'

Irena turned on him sharply 'Jesus hasn't even had a hot drink yet. Go outside with Simon and get everyone to sit down in an orderly queue. Mary, Hannah you help me!'

She paused and her voice softened 'Tell them he won't be long! Jesus will see them all. They don't need to fret!'

As Andrew and Simon hurried away she turned to Jesus with a hot cup of sweet lemon tea. 'Drink this, and there's new bread in the oven. I won't have you facing that lot on an empty stomach.'

Jesus smiled. 'What a treasure you are!' he said happily. And it was Irena's turn to blush.

News that Jesus had returned had spread throughout Galilee and people came to Simon's house from far and wide. Soon the little town was full to bursting with people carrying or supporting their loved ones, all looking for Jesus.

Tabitha very quickly sold out of food and returned home to make more and other women hastened to make some money by setting up stalls of food outside their houses. The pilgrims were anxious and noisy when they arrived but with firm, gentle handling they soon settled down to wait their turn. But their numbers never got less and Irena and Mary watched anxiously as Jesus grew more and more tired.

He worked all day and well into the night before he got to the end of the queue and then after a quick meal he announced that he needed to get away for while.

Irena began to fuss anxiously but Jesus silenced her with a look. 'Every time I heal I give God's love and bit by bit I feel it draining from my body. I am very tired but food and sleep will not replenish what has gone. This can only be done by prayer. I need to pray!' he looked down at Irena 'and I need you to understand.'

'I do!' she said 'I do! But I can't bear to see you so weak!'

It was early morning before he returned and to Irena's relief he did look refreshed. She, on the other hand, looked exhausted. Jesus looked at her with compassion 'You didn't sleep last night did you?'

She shook her head.

''Next time you can't sleep' he said 'Don't waste the night. Prayer will give you strength if sleep fails.'

The crowds were even worse this day. They had come earlier because sunset would bring in the Sabbath and they needed to get home before then.

As the day drew on a sense of frenzy descended on the waiting people. In the middle of the afternoon it began to rain but rather than look for shelter elsewhere everybody tried to squeeze into Simon's house. It was then that Jesus' family arrived from Nazareth.

Horrified by the frenzied crowds and unable to reach her son, Mary sent a message to Jesus.

'Master' said Judas 'your mother and brothers are outside.'

Jesus paused in his work and the people clutched at his clothing to prevent him from leaving them. Jesus smiled down at them all 'You are all as important to me as my mother and my brothers. Do not concern yourselves. I will not go to them until my work here is done.'

They all breathed a sigh of relief as Jesus resumed his work and Irena went out the back way and found Mary and the family and led them into the courtyard.

Later with the crowds leaving for their homes, Jesus was able to go out into the courtyard to find them all. His face was pale with exhaustion and Mary ran to him and clutched him to her.

'Jesus' she wept 'you can't go on like this. It is too much!'

'You are right Mother' Jesus agreed sadly 'On days like this I lose all my strength and I am too tired to teach my disciples.'

'Let them help more' suggested Mary 'you are wearing yourself out.'

'I will pray about it' promised Jesus. 'My father will tell me what to do! Now' he said pulling himself together 'I must wash and then we must go to the synagogue.'

As Jesus, flanked by his brothers and his disciples, entered the synagogue he was greeted with both warmth and affection by Jairus, the chazzan. It wasn't until after the service that they noticed Simon, the Pharisee from Magdala, standing at the back of the synagogue in huddled conversation with a group of scribes and Pharisees from Capernaum. They stopped talking as he walked past and then began again when he left the building.

The next morning Jesus seemed both refreshed and determined and set off once more with his brothers and with a few of his disciples to the synagogue. As he entered the building people leaned forward to touch his clothing as he passed and the Pharisees pursed their lips in disapproval. That sort of thing should be reserved for the Torah they whispered among themselves.

The service began and when it came to the reading from the prophets Jairus looked to Jesus and Jesus nodded. He stood up and walked to the front, but just as he was about the read a man right in the front close to the reading desk stood up. Tears were coursing down his face and he help up a withered arm for all to see.

Jesus paused and looked at the man. The distress in the man's face was evident. He did not want to be doing this. Still silent Jesus looked around the synagogue and saw the scribes and the Pharisees watching intently. It was a trap. They had put the man there to see what Jesus would do. Jesus was angry. He beckoned to the man 'Come and stand here so all may see' he said.

The man moved hesitantly forward and Jesus spoke out loud to the congregation 'Is is lawful on the Sabbath to do good or to do harm?'

'To do good' they chorused.

'Is it lawful on the Sabbath' continued Jesus 'to save life or to kill?'

'To save life!' They were smiling now and looking round at the scowling Pharisees.

Jesus was grieved by the hardness of heart that had led to this happening. He turned to the man 'Stretch out your hand' he demanded and the man embarrassed at being forced into the situation gingerly lifted his arm.

'Stretch it out!' demanded Jesus again and as the man did as he was asked so everyone in the congregation watched as the arm and the hand became strong once more. The fingers uncurled and the flesh plumped up and became firm.

A gasp went through the congregation and the faces of the Pharisees hardened with anger. One of them stood up. 'Have you no regard for our laws?' he questioned. 'You and your so called disciples flout them everywhere you go!'

Jesus looked at him calmly. 'I have not come to destroy the law nor the teachings of the prophets. I have come to fulfil them!'

Another gasp rippled through the men.

'I tell you' continued Jesus 'not one iota, not none dot will pass from the law until all is accomplished.' He looked again at the Pharisees. 'A teacher who causes a man to hate the law will be called the least in the Kingdom of Heaven but a teacher who shows a man how to love the law will be called great.'

Turning again to the congregation he said firmly 'Unless the law is written on your hearts and your righteousness exceeds that of the scribes and Pharisees, you will never enter the Kingdom of Heaven.'

Another Pharisee sprang to his feet almost spluttering in his anger. 'And now' he said 'you have broken our Sabbath laws. You have worked and we have all been witnesses.'

'That is true' agreed Jesus 'but the law that demands that we rest on the Sabbath was made for our benefit to give us a day of refreshment and peace. The Sabbath was made for man not man for the Sabbath!'

He looked at them all and smiled 'I too need a rest from my work but what I did I did to glorify God.'

Then he chuckled and said to the Pharisees 'Have you heard that in Jerusalem the scholars are discussing whether or not they should eat an egg that has been laid on the Sabbath, because, as my brother tells me, they are debating whether the hen has been working?'

There was an amazed silence and then Jairus began to laugh. Soon the whole congregation was laughing and the group of scribes and Pharisees exchanged hurried glances and slipped away through the back door. They had intended making Jesus out to be a charlatan but instead it was they who had lost face.

It was not something they would find easy to forgive.

CHAPTER FIFTEEN

Just before sunset heralded the end of the Sabbath Jesus walked down to the shore and turned towards Bethsaida and the hills beyond. By the time the people had left their houses he was out of sight.

The disciples were not unduly concerned. They had become accustomed to Jesus' need to find a deserted place in which to pray.

'Now more than ever' said John 'he will need to talk to God.'

There was no sign of him the following day either, but the next morning as the disciples stood on the quay beside one of Simon's boats they saw him walking in the shallows of the water towards them. He looked refreshed and determined and was delighted to find them waiting and ready to go.

'Let us go up to Bethsaida today!' he said. 'There are many people who are too infirm to walk here, so we will go to them!'

They took the road and passed through the customs toll. Matthew was pleased to see that an old friend had taken over the post and hung back from the others for a while as he caught up on the local gossip.

When he joined the others again he was accompanied by two men. They had all been walking quickly and were gasping for breath. 'Jesus!' called Matthew as he arrived 'these two men are disciples of John the Baptist. They have been looking for you!'

The two men dropped to their knees. 'Master!' one of them gasped 'John the Baptist has been arrested!'

A shudder of dismay rippled through the group. Jesus helped the men to their feet 'Come off the road' he said 'and tell me what has happened!'

'After your baptism Master, John moved up the Jordan valley to Bannaeus' said one.

'That took him into Herod's territory' said the other 'and almost every day we would see one or other of his officials, or even Herod himself, crossing the ford as they journeyed from Maccherus to Tiberias and Sepphoris.'

'John seemed to get angrier every day!' said the first. 'He was alright when he was baptising and telling people about you but when Herod or one of his men rode by he would work himself into a frenzy.'

'It was far worse when Herodias came by!' the two men were in complete agreement.

'Why?' Andrew asked bewildered.

'Because' explained James 'she divorced Herod's brother Philip and left him to go and live with Herod. She and her daughter!'

'That's it exactly!' said the first of John's disciples. 'John, our master, told everyone who would listen, that it was a disgrace that the country's leaders should behave with such immorality.'

'That wouldn't have made him popular with Herod!' said John.

'It's Herodias he had trouble with! She hates him!'

'And now!' said the other 'she got her way and he's been arrested to keep him quiet.'

'Where is he now?' asked Jesus.

'They took him to Maccherus. He's in the dungeon there' they answered.

'We were allowed to visit him yesterday' said one. 'He's very depressed! He thinks he's let you down.'

'What did he say?' Jesus was concerned.

'He said' said one 'if you're not the Messiah then he has not done what God has sent him to do and now he's allowed himself to be arrested he says he will have failed!'

Jesus smiled 'Your master has done his work well, but don't take my word for it. Stay with us today. Listen and watch and make up your own minds. Then you can go and tell John so that he too can decide.'

They continued along the road together and as they entered Bethsaida they were greeted with enthusiasm. So many people from the town had already visited Capernaum bringing their sick that there were friendly, grateful faces in every doorway. Only outside the little square building that served as a synagogue was there any hostility, but Jesus and his group passed by with a smile and settled themselves on the steps of John and James' family home. Here the people of the town found them and brought their sick, the elderly, the lame and the blind.

All who came were healed and the disciples, seeing it all afresh through the eyes of John's disciples, were amazed at the power and proud of the person. There surely could be no doubt that Jesus was the greatest leader Israel had ever seen and one day the whole world would know it.

By the end of the day Jesus called John's two followers over to him. 'Go now and tell John what you have seen' he said. 'Tell him that the blind receive their sight, the lame walk, the deaf hear, the dead are raised up and the poor have good news preached to them. Tell him too' he continued 'that he will be greatly blessed. He has done his work well. He need not be ashamed of me or for himself. It is as God ordered!'

When John's messengers had gone, Jesus spoke to his disciples. 'You have all been out to the desert to see John, to listen to him and to be baptised by him. He was not a soft man, was he? He spoke what he believed to be the truth no matter who was there. He didn't mince his words. He was straight and true.'

'What was he?' Jesus demanded 'A prophet? Yes and far more than a prophet! He was the one foretold to herald the Messiah and it was inevitable that he would meet with trouble. There are some people who are always looking for trouble. They complained about John because he lived roughly and ate sparingly and they complain about me and say I am a glutton and a drunkard and a friend of tax collectors and sinners!'

'John has been arrested and his end is near. Soon it will be my time!'

Mary reached out and clutched at Jesus' hand, her face drained of its colour. 'Don't say it!' she gasped.

The disciples were shocked.

Jesus looked at them all. His eyes were sombre with sadness. 'I need to take you away somewhere where we can be alone so that I can prepare you all for the times ahead. Tomorrow we will leave from Simon's house early in the morning before the town is awake.' He turned to Mary 'can you prepare food for at least three days? We'll all help you carry it!'

'Of course we can!' she replied. 'We'll be ready in the morning.

***

The next morning the small group left Capernaum and starting around Magdala took the hill road towards Mt Tabor. 'We need to go somewhere where we are not known.' Jesus was setting a fast pace and by midday they reached the well outside the village of Nain. They drew some water to drink and shared some bread and dried fish and then stood ready to move once more.

Jesus pointed to the southwest 'We'll walk a few miles into the hills over there and then we can make our plans.' He looked around at them all 'We can't stay here. It won't be long before the women come to get water.'

'There's a group coming now' called Andrew pointing.

There was indeed a small group leaving the little town and coming in their direction, but it was not a group of women. 'It's a funeral!' said James and the group stood and watched quietly out of respect.

The chazzan walked ahead and he was followed by a woman who was sobbing so much she could barely walk. Two men followed on behind carrying a bier. As they grew closer the disciples could see that there was the body of a young man on the bier. He could only be about seventeen. The woman, obviously his mother, was distraught. There were no other friends or relatives. The path they were taking passed the well on its way to the caves in the hills.

The chazzan glanced at the men and nodded his head as he passed. The woman looked up and caught Jesus' eyes, and then she stopped so suddenly that the two men carrying the bier almost fell.

'Are you the teacher from Capernaum?' she gasped between her tears.

'I am' replied Jesus quietly.

'Help me!' begged the woman 'Please help me!' she turned to the bier. 'This is my only son. I am a widow and my son is my reason for living. Now he is dead. What can I do?' She fell on her knees 'You can help. I know you can!'

Jesus leant down and took her hands pulling her gently to her feet. 'Come with me!' he said and putting his arm around her to stop her from falling he led her to the bier.

The chazzan had turned to discover that he was not being followed and began to walk back to see what was happening. The disciples stepped tentatively towards the bier. What could Jesus do?

Simon glanced at James and John. Their faces were white with anticipation. They knew.

Jesus and the boy's mother were at the bier. She had begun to weep again.

'Don't weep!' said Jesus and his voice was filled with compassion. He reached out and touched the bier.

'Young man' he said loudly 'Get up!'

The young man immediately opened his eyes and began to stretch as though waking from a long sleep. In panic the two men almost dropped the bier onto the ground. They stepped back. Their eyes were round and their mouths open. As though it were nothing untoward the young man continued to stretch and then sat up and got to his feet. His mother fell into his arms.

'My son!' she sobbed.

The disciples and the chazzan stood as though transfixed.

Jesus put his arms around mother and son. 'It is God's will that you live' he said to the young man and turning to the woman 'It was your faith that saved him.'

The chazzan ran forward and Jesus stepped back. 'Tell no one what has happened here today' he demanded 'Go to your homes and say nothing.'

'Come!' he said turning to the disciples 'They won't be able to keep quiet. We must go quickly or we will never be allowed to be alone again!'

Still shocked, the disciples picked up their belongings and followed him. No one spoke. What was there to say?

***

They went as far and as quickly as they could into the hills to the south of the village. Soon there was nothing but narrow terraces and boulder strewn slopes. They met a shepherd leading a ragged flock of sheep and goats but he didn't even acknowledge their presence and walked past them without a glance.

There were several low caves in the area and Jesus looked around and said 'Let us camp here for a few days. We can use the caves for shelter and we can all scout around for firewood. We can stay until the food runs out!'

As they sat around the fire later Jesus began to speak. 'The time has come' he said 'I need your help and I think that you are all nearly ready to go out on your own.'

'Go out where?' demanded Simon.

'On our own?' questioned Thomas.

'No!' said James 'We're not ready yet! We've done nothing but control the crowds. We can't teach. We can't heal!' There was a panic in his voice.

Jesus was quiet, he smiled and then he spoke. 'You have all been chosen for this task. You may think that it was your decision to follow me. But no, I chose you and I chose you with great care.'

'Nothing is impossible if you have faith. Why' he said with a laugh 'if you said to this hill, get up from here and throw yourself into the sea and, if you really believed it, it would happen.'

They all laughed.

'All you have to do' he continued, 'is to believe in the power of God's love and trust in his goodness and there will be nothing that you can't do.'

'Matthew is writing down your sayings' said John. 'We could learn them by heart.'

'You have listened to me and you have watched me. What Matthew has written will be a great help but if you go out from here in my name the words you say will come to you and you will have the power to heal as I have done.'

'We'll be able to heal?' asked Andrew incredulously.

'Whatever you ask in my name will be granted to you' said Jesus. 'God will hear you when you ask.'

'That is something you must learn' he continued 'Everything you do and say must be in the power of God and you can only do that if you pray and never cease from praying.'

'Our whole life has to become a prayer' mused John. 'I like that idea!'

Jesus smiled, 'You've seen me go away to find time alone in order to pray. Have I ever looked as if it was a chore?'

'Just the opposite' said Simon 'You look as if you're going to heaven itself!'

'That's it! Simon. That's exactly it!' Jesus was pleased. 'When you pray you go into the presence of God and when you are in the presence of God you are in heaven.'

'And if our whole life is a prayer then we are in the Kingdom' John was excited. 'But' he said and his smile faded 'prayer is hard. Why should God take any notice of what I have to say?'

'Because God cares about you' replied Jesus. 'If you ask, it will be given to you. Seek and you will find. Knock and the door will be opened to you! For everyone who asks receives, and he who seeks finds and to him who knocks it will be opened.'

'Simon!' he said, 'You are a father. So are you James and Nathaniel. If one of your children asks you for a fish would you give them a snake? Or if they ask for an egg would you give them a scorpion?'

'Of course you wouldn't' he continued with a smile 'and if you wouldn't why should you think that God would? If you know how to treat your children with love just think how much more generously God will treat you.'

'You are going out as God's messengers into a world that can be hostile and dangerous. You must travel in this world without fear. But when you pray, you take God with you and he will be there to comfort you and give you strength.'

'Go now!' he said to them all 'Find a place to be alone and open your hearts to God and ask him to fill you with his love. Remember, if you ask it will be given to you.'

He got to his feet and the look he gave them was filled with pride. 'Now begins the most exciting journey of your life. Surround yourself with the love of God, put you hand into his hand and go! Enter the Kingdom of Heaven!'

CHAPTER SIXTEEN

Two days later the disciples, almost sick with nervous anticipation, left the camp in pairs. They were to stay in Galilee and to take nothing with them, save only for the love of God. No money. No food. 'If the labourer is worthy of his hire' said Jesus 'the people you serve will take care of you.'

They had watched Jesus and wondered at the power they knew him to have received from God. Now it was their turn. They were his disciples and in his name they were being sent out. They had seen what this power could do, but would they be found wanting? Would they be able to heal? Would the people listen when they preached? They were scared! Nobody wanted to let Jesus down.

When he had seen the last of the pairs disappear along the sheep paths that led towards to towns and villages of Galilee, Jesus and the two women walked back to Capernaum. The disciples would return in a week's time.

Back in Capernaum Jesus was keen to hear news of John the Baptist. But the only news that had filtered back to the town was that John was still in the fortress at Maccherus and that Herod himself, anxious not to harm a prophet, was standing up against Herodias' continual demands to have John killed and be done with it.

The people in the street didn't think John stood a chance. They knew Herod was stubborn but they knew Herodias' hate was stronger. Bets were being placed over mugs of wine at the inn. 'When a wife has made up her mind' they reasoned 'what hope does a poor husband have!'

Herodias saw her chance that very week. It was Herod's birthday and guests had been arriving at Maccherus for days. Food was delivered in wagons. Oysters and fish from Joppa, mushrooms and venison from Lebanon, crushed ice from Mount Hermon, fat juicy figs from Jericho, lamb from the Judean hills, honey, pigeons, sweet meats, everything Herod desired; the cooks, the entertainers and the guests continued to arrive. Herod was anxious to impress and Herodias did her best to turn the ugly old fortress in the desert into a palace of dreams.

'When will we ever move from here?' she moaned 'Will Sepphoris never be ready?'

After the sophistication of Jerusalem she and her daughter Salome hated the desert life and considered Herod's friends boorish. Still Herod himself was not as boring as his gentle brother Philip. What a wimp he was! And Herod was ambitious and they could at least share those ambitions together.

The day of the birthday dawned fair. It was warm enough for the women to gather on the terraces and sip fruit cordials through crushed ice. The desert wind was dry and cooling and the muslin drapes sheltered them from the fierce rays of the sun.

Herod and his male guests remained in the Great Hall where lush cushions were piled around low tables groaning with food. The drinking started early that day.

As the morning drew on some of the men, bleary eyed with drink, became noisy. Bursts of raucous laughter broke out as bawdy jokes were bandied about and the scantily clad serving wenches had to keep well out of arm's way as they scurried in and out with fresh jugs of wine and food.

Herod frowned. It was essential that things didn't get out of hand. Some of his most important guests could well disapprove if the day sank into pure debauchery. He hastily beckoned to a serving girl to fill up the mugs of those men closest to him on the top table. 'Hold back on the others' he ordered 'Give them food!'

The troop of dancing girls from Idumaea were a hit but the jugglers that followed were booed out of the hall. Herod looked up and saw Salome watching from the doorway. He crooked a finger at her and she sauntered over. At sixteen she was already aware of her body and her eyes, black with kohl, were sultry and inviting.

As she came close to her step father she bent over to listen to what he had to say and Prince Hazim sitting close by was transfixed by the closeness of her perfumed and plump young body.

'Go and tell your mother to send the dancers back quickly' said Herod and watching the Prince out of the corner of his eyes he added 'And then come back yourself and help me entertain these important guests!'

Salome took her time. She walked slowly out of the room and was even slower when she returned. Only when she was sure that every man was watching her did she sit down next to Prince Hazim and gaze into his eyes.

Herod breathed a sigh of relief. If the Prince was happy all would be well. He allowed himself to relax and a serving girl filled his mug with wine which he downed in one large draught.

The party grew perceptibly noisier but Prince Hazim was well occupied. Salome knew instinctively how to hold a man's attention. It was only later when the jugglers dared to return and everybody laughed them out of the room before they even had a chance to start, that Prince Hazim leaned across to Herod and said 'Let Salome dance! I'd consider it a great favour if you would allow her to show us just how a woman should dance.' He dropped his voice 'It could even make the stones from my quarry reach your building projects more quickly.'

Herod didn't hesitate. 'Salome' he ordered 'Get up and dance for us!'

But Salome was offended. Herod could be so gross. Who did he think he was ordering her about like that? She remained seated and looked at her step father with contempt. Her eyes had become slits of black hate.

Realising that he had had too much to drink and that he had made a monumental mistake Herod hastily back tracked. 'I know it is beneath someone of your station in life' he wheedled 'but, Salome, you would be doing me a great favour! Prince Hazim here has asked for you especially!'

Salome still refused to move. 'What's in it for me?' she asked sullenly.

'Anything you want!' said Herod and then seeing a gleam appear in her eyes, 'Anything' he repeated, 'Even up to half my kingdom.'

Prince Hazim and the guests near to Herod laughed 'What a generous man you are!' they said. 'She could fleece you!'

Salome slowly got to her feet. 'I'll dance!' she said, and removing her sandals she walked barefooted into the middle of the smooth tiled floor. As she walked she picked up her long hair and twisting it deftly with her hand she lifted her arms and fastened her hair high on her head. One by one the men stopped talking and turned to watch as this picture of youthful loveliness stood before them.

Then she began to dance. She began in silence but when the musicians saw her dancing they picked up the rhythm and began to play. She was light on her feet and her young body was supple and the men caught their breath. Herod's eyes, red rimmed with drink, now beamed with pride.

Salome took her muslin stole and held it high above her head as she danced and swayed to the rhythm of the music. The men groaned as her young breasts bounced out of the flimsy top that enclosed them. Oblivious, Salome whirled and danced as the rhythm picked up, her nimble feet flying around the room. And then her hair came undone and tumbled over her shoulders and she sank on to the floor.

The applause was tumultuous. The men clapped and banged their mugs on the table. Herod was beside himself with pride. He stood up and walked across the room and pulled Salome to her feet. 'What a birthday present!' he said and he turned to face his guests. 'My step daughter!' he announced and the clapping and banging began again.

As he escorted Salome back to his table she rearranged her clothes and stood demurely in front of Prince Hazim looking at him coyly under her eye lashes. He laughed 'Ask for your reward!' he said 'Let's see if your generous step father will keep his word!'

'I will!' she agreed 'but first I must go to my mother' and she slipped from Herod's grasp and ran from the room.

Herod sank on to the cushions and reached for his wine. 'What a day!' he thought as his guests all leaned over to congratulate him. 'What a day!'

Herodias was in the passage way leading from the Great Hall. Alerted by the noisy applause she had been on her way to see what was happening. Her anger at seeing her daughter exposing herself in such company soon evaporated when she heard the whole story and her eyes became calculating. This was definitely an opportunity not to be missed.

'Wait here!' she ordered her daughter and then turned and went in to the kitchen returning with a large silver platter. Giving it to Salome she said 'Take this into Herod and in a loud voice, so that everyone can hear, remind him of his promise and then ask for the head of the Baptist to be presented to you in this plate.'

Salome gagged 'I couldn't ask that!' she shuddered.

'You can and you will' ordered Herodias fiercely 'This is the chance I've been waiting for.'

'Mother! We could ask for gold! Let me ask for gold' begged Salome.

'Gold!' Herodias spat. 'Gold and riches will be nothing but a bad taste in my mouth as long as that man continues to live. He has to go!' She took hold of Salome's shoulders and shook her 'You don't want to upset me do you?'

'No mother!' Salome cringed back. Herodias upset was not pleasant.

'Go on! Do it now!' ordered Herodias pushing her towards the door. 'Remember! Speak up!'

From the way Salome walked into the room no one would have guessed that her stomach was churning. She stood in front of Herod and his guests and held up the platter. 'I've decided' she said calmly.

Herod looked up from his wine 'Go on' he said with a dismissive wave of his hand. 'Tell us what you wish!'

'I want' her voice was imperious 'the head of John the Baptist brought to me on this platter.'

There was a sudden stillness in the room.

The Prince Hazim slapped his leg in delight and turned to a horrified Herod 'She's got you there old boy! What are you going to do now?'

'This is too much!' spluttered Herod 'He's a holy man!'

'You promised!' Salome was calm and very self possessed. 'You said anything up to half your kingdom.'

'I know I did!' Herod tried to reason 'but I expected you to ask for money, or jewellery or even land. Not the death of a prophet!' he shuddered.

'Isn't Herod Antipas a man of his word then?' asked Prince Hazim feigning innocence and enjoying every moment of the drama.

Herod groaned. He stood up 'Never let it be said that Herod cannot keep his promise.' He called the two guards who were standing motionless by the passage door. 'Take this platter' he ordered 'and return with the head of the Baptist.'

As the guards marched out Herod sank down on his cushions. Salome stood her ground and Prince Hazim gave her an admiring glance. The rest of the guests were perceptibly quieter.

It was a good ten minutes before the men returned and as they entered several of the guests hastily clasped their hands over their mouths and gagged. Others got to their feet and fled the room.

Salome remained pale and rigid and as the platter was brought towards her she stared over the head of the guards.

The colour had drained from Herod's face completely and he pushed his wine away and struggled to his feet. Looking at the platter and the still, proud face of the prophet, Herod's face crumpled and he turned and strode out of the room.

Prince Hazim lay back on his cushions and, as Salome left the room carrying her grizzly trophy, he began to clap very slowly.

***

Jesus heard the news the same day. Mary found him on the beach alone. She sat down on a boulder beside him and, as the waters of the peaceful lake lapped gently on the stones, she told him what she had heard.

Jesus put his head in his hands and a shudder shook his body. Mary put up a hand to touch is arm and they stayed like that together until the sun dipped down behind the hills.

CHAPTER SEVENTEEN

John and Andrew were the first to return. Bursting with suppressed excitement they couldn't keep the smiles of delight from their faces. They were followed soon afterwards by Simon and James and two by two they all returned to Capernaum. Irena was kept busy serving bread, dried fish and succulent black figs and with a smile hovering around his mouth Jesus watched them all as they ravenously devoured the food, exchanged news and talked excitedly about their experiences.

'News of what you have been doing has reached us here in Capernaum' said Jesus. 'The stories I've heard have been so amazing I could swear I saw the devil himself fall from the sky!'

They all laughed. But Simon soon looked serious 'It's not really a joke is it?' he said 'Some of the things we've done must be sorely testing the devil!' He turned to Jesus 'Who would have thought that love was so powerful? We've all done things in your name that have frightened us!'

'But it made my heart feel good' said John with a wide grin 'I feel as though God had me in the palm of his hand. I felt so safe and somehow' he looked up at Jesus 'I knew you were there with me too!'

'Yes!' agreed Simon 'I felt you were by my side all the time.'

Jesus smiled 'I knew how nervous you were!'

'You mean you were there?' asked Simon.

'I told you all that the harvest is plentiful but the labourers are few. If you go out into the world in my name I will always be working by your side.' Jesus looked around at them all 'Until the day comes when all men have entered the Kingdom, we will go on taking my Father's love in to the world, and we will do it together!'

Then Jesus gestured to the cushions 'Come and sit down for a moment' he said. 'In the midst of your joy something has happened of great sadness.'

Instantly quiet and serious all the men sank on to the cushions and listened in horror to the report of John's death. Matthew was the first to speak 'We've all embarked on a very dangerous mission then' he said 'What has happened to John could well happen to you Jesus, or to us.' He spread his arm around the room and the disciples all exchanged anxious glances.

Jesus spoke quietly 'If you want to go home, now is the time to go! I would not have you continue if your heart is afraid.'

Simon spoke up 'We have already learnt that when we are afraid you are there by our side and we have seen at first hand the immense power of God's love. If we are on God's side how can anyone stand against us!'

Jesus' smile was sad 'What God wants for us may not be what we want. Will you stand the test?'

Simon was eager 'I will always be true' he said 'you can count on me!'

'I do' said Jesus 'more than you can ever know.'

Irena bustled into the room and the men looked round smiling affectionately as she apologised for disturbing them. 'It's the people' she said hurriedly 'While you've been talking hundreds of them have been gathering outside. Can't you hear them?'

It was only then that they realised that the dull roar in the background that had been growing louder as they talked was the noise of many voices. Jesus glanced at Simon 'Just to show you how much I count on you' he said 'can you slip out the back way? Take Andrew with you and get the boat ready. We will follow you in a few minutes and then we can get away in the boat.'

He looked around at them all. 'You are full of news. We have a lot to talk about and we need to take time apart. We must go somewhere where we can be alone.'

'Go on Simon!' he said with a grin 'I'm sure you've been missing your beloved boat! Go and get her ready, but be quick about it!'

The boat slipped quietly away from the quay and Simon was already raising the sail before the crowd realised what had happened. As soon as the boat was spotted there was a huge surge of people towards the beach and a groan of despair from the sick and those who carried them as they watched the boat skim across the water.

'Which direction are they going?' called a voice from the back.

'East!' came the reply from the beach 'they're going across the lake to the hills.'

Those who were carrying the sick gave another groan and Irena bustled out of the house. 'He'll be back!' she said 'They just need a break. You people never leave him alone!'

'I'm waiting!' A large man with bandages around his foot sat down with a thump. 'Even if I have to wait all day!'

Irena looked content. 'Tabitha sells food from her stall on the quay. Those of you who decide to stay will be well provided for.' She turned back in to the house.

A group of young men were talking excitedly. 'Jonah says he thinks Jesus is the Messiah!' said one.

'So does Ephraim' said another.

'I've only heard stories of what he can do' said a third. 'I hoped I might see something today to help me make up my mind!'

'It wouldn't take us long, perhaps a couple of hours, to walk round the lake and find them.'

'You're right! What are we waiting for?'

They left at a run; first along the beach and then as rushes impeded their way they sprinted on to the Bethsaida road. Others seeing them go realised at once what they intended doing. Soon all those fit enough to walk were streaming away from Capernaum and running in to the morning sun. Far ahead of them the boat grew smaller and soon all that could be seen clearly was the little red sail at the foot of the purple shaded hills in the East.

Unaware of the crowds intentions Jesus and the disciples breathed in the fresh morning air and their spirits soared as the boat sped across the water towards the far shore.

As they drew near Simon steered the boat on to a small beach and everyone jumped out, knee deep in the water, and together they pulled the boat on to the beach. They then climbed the grassy banks up the hillside until they found a level area on which to sit and relax and gaze out across the lake.

Jesus allowed them to talk. All of them were so excited. They had performed miracles; people had been healed, blind men were now able to see, devils had left those possessed. Each one of them had, by calling on the name of Jesus, been able to do these wondrous things. Even Thomas, who always needed a logical explanation, had done things that defied logic.

'You were true to your word' said Judas catching Jesus' gaze 'I've experienced for myself the power of love. I would never have believed it possible!'

Jesus smiled. 'You are all now instruments of God's love in the world' he said 'Love in a world full of fear, of hate and of evil. It seems as insignificant as a grain of salt would be if dropped in to the lake. But' he looked around 'you all know how important salt is. It enhances flavour, it cleanses and it can cure.'

'And it is very expensive!' muttered James.

'Indeed it is James!' laughed Jesus 'It's expensive because it is hard won. Men have to work long, hard hours in appalling conditions to extract it. Salt is very precious, especially here in our hot, dry land.'

'You are like salt' he continued 'the salt of the earth. With the love of God you will go into the world to enhance people's lives, to cleanse and to cure. But as you all know, if salt loses its flavour its good for nothing but to be trodden under foot. It is up to you to make sure that you retain the saltiness, that God's love in you is always vibrant and alive.'

'How can we do that?' demanded John anxiously 'I hadn't realised how tired you can get when you're trying to care for people.'

'It's only possible through prayer' replied Jesus 'when you are too tired even to eat, surround yourself in God and pray.' He looked around at their eager faces. 'Through prayer you will receive the bread of life and that will give you back your energy, your life.'

'Tell me!' he continued 'Were you received with kindness on your journeys?'

All the disciples tried to reply at once as memories of their mission flooded to the fore. Their experiences were mixed. 'Just remember' Jesus said 'If people reject you they also reject me! If they accept you they are saying "Yes" to me! We are in this together!'

'Some people were insulting. I found it hard to keep my temper' said John flushing at the memory.

'Forgive them John! And move on' Jesus replied.

'How many times should we forgive someone?' asked Simon 'Seven times?'

'No Simon!' said Jesus with a smile 'seventy times seven!'

'This business of loving gets harder every day!' replied Simon ruefully.

'Or more exciting' interrupted John 'it depends how you look at it!'

Andrew suddenly stood up and looked down over to the northern shore line. 'I thought I saw movement' he said pointing 'Look the crowds have followed us!'

Jesus also stood. The people were straggling along the shore towards them. 'There are hundreds of them!' he said 'and they look so tired!'

It was the fit, young men who reached them first. In fact it was mostly men who had made the journey and as they had walked with such urgency they collapsed on to the grass with exhaustion when they arrived.

Jesus and his disciples were amazed by the numbers of people that had followed them. Surely there were thousands, not hundreds! Some had come with sick friends and relatives, but not many. The journey had been too punishing for the sick. Jesus began almost immediately to heal those who came to him and after a moment's hesitation the disciples joined in.

It was well in to the afternoon before the last stragglers arrived. Jesus watched them climb the slope and slump down on the grass. Full of compassion he turned to the disciples. 'They are so tired and they must be hungry. We must feed them all!'

'But we're miles from the villages. How are we going to buy any food?' exclaimed Philip 'and we haven't got nearly enough money!'

'Some of the people have food with them' said Andrew. 'This little lad here has five barley loaves and two fish, but what are they among so many?'

'Tell everybody to sit down' commanded Jesus. 'Get them as organised as you can, into groups of about fifty.'

The word was soon passed around and the people eagerly complied. They sat and looked up at Jesus expectantly. Obviously something was about to happen.

Jesus bent down to the lad. 'Will you give me your basket of food?' he asked gently. Eyes big with wonder the boy handed over his basket in silence.

Jesus nodded his thanks and taking a loaf of bread from the basket he held it high and his voice carried above the seated crowd. 'Blessed art thou, O Lord our God, King of the universe' he prayed. 'Thanks to you we have our daily bread. May it be for us the Bread of Life!'

Then he tore the soft flat loaf in half and began to tear it into pieces. As he tore, the pieces filled the boy's basket, and still he went on breaking pieces off the loaf. The disciples unwound their neck cloths and opened them out as the pieces kept coming. They stood and the bread filled the cloths. 'Give them to the people!' ordered Jesus and the disciples hurried to obey.

Those sitting close enough to see what Jesus was doing were silent with wonder. Soon the news reached even those in the back ranks and as the bread kept coming so the silence grew. The disciples moved backwards and forwards with the baskets of bread. They had started from the back and were now working among those closest to Jesus. Each man, woman or child took their portion and looked at it curiously before slowly eating. Eventually all were fed, even the disciples. Satiated and comfortable the crowd began to whisper and then bit by bit the sound increased as they all began to ponder over what had happened.

Jesus called the disciples to him. 'While they are all still sitting down go quickly and collect up the bread that hasn't been eaten.' Bewildered, the disciples did as they were told and within a few minutes they were all back with a basket or cloth full of scraps.

The small boy looked them in amazement. 'How could that all be left over?' he exclaimed finally finding his voice.

'How many tribes are there in Israel?' asked Jesus.

'Twelve of course!' said the boy looking up at the disciples.

'My disciples have gathered twelve baskets of scraps, because I want to show them that even those people that everyone else have rejected will be gathered up and brought into the Kingdom.'

He looked at the disciples 'The tax collectors, the beggars, the prostitutes and the sinners, don't leave any of them out. They must all be gathered in.'

A rumour began to ripple back through the crowd 'He's talking about the Kingdom.'

'Anyone who can do these things must be the Messiah!'

'Will he raise an army do you think?'

'He can count me in!' said one.

'And me!' said another 'I fancy having a go at those bloody Romans.'

'With his power we couldn't lose!'

'If we could get rid of the Romans we could have our own king.'

'There's no one I'd like to see as king more than this Jesus. Did you know he cured my sister? She's been ill all her life and one word from him and she's fit and well as though she hadn't ever had a moment's illness.'

'I'd go along with that' said another. 'If Jesus was king I'd follow him!'

The ripple began to grow and spread right through the crowd. The young lad pulled at Jesus' robes. 'Can I be a soldier in your army?' he asked.

'What army is that?' asked Jesus with a smile.

'When you're king!' said the boy. 'Everyone is saying you're going to be a king. They all want to join your army.'

Jesus raised his head and looked around at the crown critically. It was true that there were several groups of men huddled together and glancing his way. He patted the boy on the shoulder. 'Thank you!' he said quietly and moved quickly alongside Simon. 'I'm going into the hills' he said 'Be firm and send the crowds home. Keep Judas and young Simon close to you and away from any agitators and, when the people have gone, sail home. I'll walk back when I'm ready.'

Then he slipped in among the people, put his shawl over his head and disappeared. Simon waited to give Jesus a chance to get away and then he climbed on to a boulder and called out to the people. 'It's a long way home and if you want to get back tonight you should leave now!'

'Where's Jesus?' they demanded.

'He's gone away to pray' Simon replied.

'To pray?' the crowd were incredulous. 'We're ready to make him king. Isn't he the Messiah then?'

'Yes. I believe he is' Simon agreed 'but prayer is very important to him. He can't live without it! You might as well go home. He often stays away for days.'

It was at least an hour later before everyone had left. One group of men stayed back when all had gone. They approached Simon 'Is your master a member of the Zealot party?' they asked. Simon spoke confidently 'Jesus belongs to no party. He is his own man!'

'But two of your group are Zealots!' they persisted.

'That's true!' agreed Simon. 'But whatever any of us were we are now Jesus' men. We have seen and experienced things since we have been with him that makes mere politics insignificant!'

'So does Jesus intend raising an army?' they asked impatiently. 'We have contacts and there are Zealots all over the country ready to follow anyone who will lead them and force the infidels out of our land.'

'The only force Jesus is interested in' said Simon 'is the power of God's love.'

The group were incredulous. 'What kind of stupidity is that?' they exclaimed 'and what a waste! There were at least five thousand men here today who, after seeing that trick with the bread, would have followed him to their death!'

As they reluctantly moved off they edged towards Judas but Simon quickly stepped in front of the disciples and moved them down towards the boat. Thwarted, the group walked down the paths to follow the main body of the crowd.

It was dark before the disciples had pushed the boat out into the lake and the wind was stronger now from the West. 'We'll have to beat our way back' Simon looked out across the lake 'it won't be a quick journey!'

'We should be back by midnight though' said James. 'So let's get going!'

They could see the lights of Capernaum in the distance. It didn't look all that far away but James was wrong. They were still beating against the wind when midnight came. On one reach they went far into the middle of the lake and on the other they almost touched the shore. It was hard work and it was nearly two o'clock in the morning. They were sailing into the shore for what they calculated was the last time before they reckoned they would make the quay side.

The wind was strong and they sped towards the shore. Andrew and John were ready to swing the sail over so that the boat could go about before the water became too shallow. It was in that moment that they saw him in front of them. Wearing only his white shift in the strong warm wind and carrying his cloak Jesus was there walking on the water.

They had left him behind so it was a shock to them all to see him there. His white shift gave him a luminous look. The disciples were afraid! Turning the boat into the wind Simon gazed in disbelief. The sails flapped and the disciples were rigid with fear.

'It's Jesus!' gasped Andrew.

'It's a ghost!' exclaimed John.

Jesus raised his hand in greeting 'Don't be afraid!' he called 'It is I.'

Simon was incredulous 'is it really you Lord?' he asked.

'Yes Simon' he called 'There really is nothing to be afraid of!'

'If it really is you let me walk to you on the water as well!'

'Come then!' said Jesus 'Walk to me!'

Still in a daze Simon clambered over the side of the boat. He put his feet on the surface of the water and took a couple of steps. The other disciples gasped and Jesus put out a hand to reach him. It was as if the gasp from his friends had woken him from a dream. Simon suddenly opened his eyes wide, panic flared up for a second and then he began to sink. 'Save me Lord!' he cried out and Jesus stepped calmly forward and caught his flailing arm.

'Where is your faith Simon?' asked Jesus with a laugh. 'You started off full of confidence and then suddenly you lost it.'

As he helped Simon back on to the boat he mused 'Why is it that fishermen never learn to swim?' Then smiled at them all 'I'll come in the boat with you now' he said 'Then we can all arrive together.'

He climbed into the boat and took his usual place in the stern. Ignored, the boat was already drifting backwards so James jumped to take the tiller and they pulled in the sails. As they set off on their final tack, Simon remained slumped in the bottom of the boat. 'Everyday' he said quietly to James 'Jesus does something that is even more amazing than the day before.' He pulled his wet clothes over his head. 'I'm not sure I can cope anymore. It's all happening too fast for me!'

CHAPTER EIGHTEEN

Exhausted though he was, Simon found himself unable to sleep when they all returned home in the early hours of the morning. While those about him slept soundly, he wrapped his cloak around him and went out of the door of the house to sit on the bench that looked out on the lake. It was pitch black but he could hear the waves lapping and the leaves of the trees rustling above him.

His thoughts were confused and he was conscious of a deep seated, gnawing sense of fear. This was more than an adventure. How was it he hadn't recognised in his friend the awesome, frightening power he was now manifesting? How could a mere man command the wind and the sea, walk on water, feed so many from so little and perform so many acts of healing?

Simon groaned. There was no doubt he was frightened. How could the others sleep so soundly? He desperately needed to talk to someone!

He was still awake when dawn woke the birds and the sun's rays crept over the eastern hills. A soft footfall caused him to look up abruptly. With his cloak wrapped tightly around him against the cool morning wind, Jairus the chazzan appeared out of the shadows. Simon edged along the bench and the older man came to sit next to him.

'I came early' he said 'I need to warn Jesus that last week our local scribes sent to Jerusalem for advice about Jesus and his teaching and last night three of their top men arrived here in Capernaum' He paused as he watched while Simon digested the information. 'Jesus must be careful. These men are looking to catch him out. They want to discredit him He's becoming too influential, too popular with the crowds, and the authorities are alarmed!'

'Jesus always tell it as it is' replied Simon with a hint of pride in his voice 'I can't see him worrying too much about what a group of scribes may think!'

'Yes, you're right!' agreed Jairus with a sigh 'but I felt I should warm him anyway.'

'How do the scribes imagine they can discredit Jesus? He knows the scriptures as well as they do.'

'They'll be tripping him up and hope to make him look a fool in front of the people' confided Jairus. 'They know the only weapons they have are criticism and ridicule, but with them they think they can turn the crowds against him!'

Simon snorted 'After what he did yesterday?' he exclaimed 'I very much doubt it!'

Jairus looked up wistfully. 'I wish I had been there!' he said 'Everyone was talking about it last night. I wish I had seen it happen!'

'Don't ask me to explain what happened' Simon put his head in his hands. 'I only know that one minute he was looking at all the people and feeling sorry for them and the next minute they had all been fed; just from five loaves and two little fish!'

He looked into Jairus' eyes 'I've been awake all night trying to make sense of all that has been happening. He was my childhood friend, as well you know, and now when I look at him all I want to do is get down on my knees in awe!'

The two men sat in silence as the birds sang in the trees around them and far out on the lake they heard the mournful cry of a wild goose.

'It seems to me that Jesus has the only weapon he needs to cope with what is coming' said Jairus, standing up to leave 'The love he has in his heart is so strong I doubt if there is any thing that can stand against it!' He caught his cloak around him 'You will give him my message?'

Simon nodded 'I will!'

An hour later every street in the little town was crowded with people and Irena was anxiously remonstrating with Jesus. 'The town has never seen so many people' she reported 'And they're all here because of you!' She folded her arms across her chest. 'Herod's bound to hear of it. There'll be trouble, mark my words!'

Jesus laughed 'Don't fear Irena!' he said 'I have a feeling that Herod won't want to cross another holy man for a while. I'll be safe from him for a few weeks or so. But Simon's just told me that a deputation of scribes has come from Jerusalem to see what's going on.' He grinned 'Now that really is a threat!'

John was indignant 'Surely not!' he cried 'You can easily manage those mealy mouthed lawyers!'

Jesus was serious for a moment. 'Yes John, I can.' He paused 'For now!' Then looking around at them all he continued 'The truth is that the petty evil in men's hearts will always seek to destroy love. It cannot bear the truth. What is beginning now will grow! But we'll worry about that tomorrow.' He straightened up and went to the door

'Today I need all your help with these crowds. Come! We must make a start!'

They barely paused for breath all morning. There were so many people. By calling on the name of Jesus, the disciples were also able to heal but found it hard if a person was mentally impaired. These were all referred to Jesus and as the morning wore on he began to wilt. The sun bore down on them relentlessly and there seemed to be a large number of people who had come just to watch. They hovered around in groups as people pushed their way forward with their sick relatives and friends.

Judas moved alongside Jesus and waited until he had a chance to catch Jesus' attention. 'Jesus, the men over there in the corner are Iscari. They were members of my unit.'

Jesus looked towards the group and nodded 'I knew they were Zealots. Do you know what they want?'

'I guess they're checking you out!' smiled Judas 'They badly need a Messiah!'

Jesus smiled too 'Let's hope they're disappointed!' he said.

Just then John and Andrew pushed their way through the people surrounding Jesus, leading a large man who stumbled awkwardly as he walked. They looked anxious and harassed. A small elderly woman hurried behind clinging on to the man's tunic and a small group of black garbed men followed closely on her heels. The scribes from Jerusalem had arrived!

John tugged at Jesus' arm. 'This man is blind and dumb. He can't see us or hear us. He can't speak. He's very strong and he lashes out when he's angry, and he seems to be angry all the time!'

'Stay calm John!' Jesus stepped forward 'All this activity is making him anxious.'

He put out his hand to the man's chest and held it there quietly until the man became still. Then Jesus spoke clearly and firmly. 'Come out of him!' he said 'And leave this man in peace!'

Standing absolutely still, the man gave a deep sigh which seemed to go on forever.

The old woman caught her breath, her eyes bulging in panic. Then the man shook his head and a look of complete bewilderment crossed his face. He shook his head again and the opaque glazing seemed to fall from his eyes. He lifted his hands suddenly and put them over his ears and let out a low moan.

Still Jesus kept his hand on the man's chest and slowly the sound ended and the man became calm. He stood looking at the faces around him. The old woman pushed forward from behind and gazed up at her son in wonderment. 'Jacob!' she cried 'You can see!'

Jesus removed his hand and brought the woman forward. 'Jacob. This is your mother' he said. 'Take her home and care for her. She has cared for you all her life. Now you can show how much you love her.'

The man looked down at the little woman and putting out his arms he caught her to him and lifted her off her feet in a great bear hug. The crowd laughed at her surprise and some began to clap. Surely anyone who could work a wonder like this must be the expected Messiah! The groups of Zealots nodded to each other. There was an air of heightened expectancy.

One of the scribes from Jerusalem spoke out in a loud voice. 'Don't make the mistake of thinking this man is something special' he said contemptuously. His power must come from Beelzebub, the Prince of Demons. That is why these demons listen to him.'

Jesus looked directly at the man who had spoken. 'That argument doesn't make sense' he said 'if a kingdom is divided against itself it will fall. If the soldiers in an army begin to fight each other rather than the enemy how long do you think they will survive? If Satan casts out Satan he is divided against himself. How then will his kingdom stand?'

'But if it is by the Spirit of God that I cast out demons then the Kingdom of God has come upon you. It is here now!'

The crowd had grown silent.

Jesus' voice became stern 'You scribes spend your lives deciphering the scriptures deciding on what a man should do or not do. I tell you this; every sin, every blasphemy you can possibly think of can be forgiven. But you should beware! Those who speak against the Holy Spirit will never be forgiven. You need to decide. Is my power from Beelzebub or is it the Spirit of God working within me?'

The men in black looked startled and then one by one they turned away and huddled together to talk. Their backs were rigid with disapproval.

The large young man and his mother, who had been standing awkwardly in front of the crowds while Jesus had been speaking, slipped quietly away and everyone began talking at once.

'Did you hear that?' John exclaimed to Andrew 'I told you he could stand up to those scribes!'

Irena came bustling out from the house carrying a tray of hot bread and fish. 'If you're not coming in to eat we'll bring the food out to you!'

She glared around at the crowd. 'He's having a break!' she said firmly 'Go and get your own food!'

Jesus went down on the bench with John and Andrew. Judas joined them and, at Irena's insistence, soon all the others had detached themselves from the people and were sitting around reaching for the deliciously smelling food. At last Irena was satisfied and stood watching them with a smile of contentment.

The scribes turned back to glare at Jesus and watched as the young men enjoyed their meal. Their mouths dropped open with astonishment. They hastily conferred again and another of the scribes from Jerusalem stepped forward indignantly. 'How can you claim to be a teacher of religion, a rabbi? Why! None of you washed your hands before eating. How is it that you and your disciples do not live according to the tradition of the elders, but eat with hands that are defiled?'

Jesus looked up at them almost casually 'Isaiah was right when he spoke of hypocrites like you who honour God with their lips but not with their hearts. You forget the commandments of God but hold sacred the rules made by men.'

'How dare you!' the scribe spluttered 'Don't you realise who we are?'

Jesus stood up and called to the crowds standing around. 'Hear me all of you!'

They turned and all fell silent.

'There is nothing, no food or even dirt from the outside of a man that can defile him if it enters his body through his mouth. It can only enter his body and pass right through it, but it cannot make him unclean in the eyes of God. On the other hand if the heart of a man is evil and his thoughts are adulterous, envious, jealous, proud or foolish then that man is defiled indeed. It is not what is on the outside of a man that defiles him it is what comes from the inside, from his heart.'

And then Jesus sat down and, taking a piece of fish from the tray, smiled at the disciples and said 'Eat! They won't go away but we need to keep our strength up. There are so many people still to see!'

It was Irena that shooed them off 'I told all you lot to leave him alone!' she shouted at them. 'Now go off and get your own food and don't forget to wash your hands!'

The crowd laughed and the scribes scurried off, their faces tight with indignation and embarrassment. Judas' Iscari friends were delighted. They too moved off but their demeanour, in contrast, was almost euphoric. Surely only a true Son of David would have the confidence to tackle the religious lawyers. The future was looking good!

***

Jesus was right, the scribes didn't go away. They stayed in the background for the rest of the day and watched as

Jesus talked to those who came to him, comforted them and healed their sick.

He grew visibly weaker as the day wore on. 'Take a break now Jesus' Simon urged him. 'We could go out in the boat. You need to stop working!'

'Not now Simon' said Jesus wearily 'today I must work. These people have been bound by superstition and restrictive laws all their lives. They are carrying burdens too heavy to bear. While I can I must work to set them free!'

Nothing anyone could say would stop him and, although he moved into the house when darkness fell, he continued to work late into the evening.

The scribes eventually left for their beds, but before they left they fired a parting shot. 'Look at him! He's working like a man possessed. You'll soon realise we were right!'

The disciples exchanged anxious glances, but Jesus didn't hear the exchange. He was too busy, too tired.

Just then Hannah beckoned to Simon 'Mary and Jesus' brothers are here!' she whispered.

'Thank goodness!' exclaimed Simon 'Now he'll stop.' He clasped Hannah's hands 'I'll go and tell him' and he turned over to Jesus.

'Jesus!' he had to speak loudly to catch Jesus' attention 'Jesus! Your mother and your brothers are here asking for you!'

Those who had not been seen groaned. They had waited all day and now Jesus would go and they wouldn't be seen. Jesus looked around at them all. 'Never fear!' he said 'You are as important to me as my family. Indeed you are all my family. I will stay with you as long as you need me.'

He looked up at Simon 'Tell my mother!'

Crestfallen Simon turned away and hurried out of the house. 'He won't come yet!' he exclaimed 'He's determined to see everyone before he rests.'

Irena clutched at Mary's arm 'He's very tired. I'm afraid for him!'

Mary looked at her 'I'll go and see for myself' she said and edged her way into the house to the edge of the crowd.

As though feeling her presence in the room Jesus looked up and caught her eye. 'Not yet!' he said with a tired smile.

'Soon though!' agreed his mother looking with compassion at the weariness in her son's eyes 'Make it soon!'

Jesus nodded 'When I've seen everyone I will rest.'

CHAPTER NINETEEN

'When this Sabbath is over I will take my disciples north.'

The women were clustered around Jesus. Mary stood in the doorway clutching a large pile of washing and the others were perched on the edges of stools in Irena's back room.

'Would you be able to prepare things for us to take?' he asked. 'We will all need bed rolls and warm clothes for the winter. We will be going away for quite a while, somewhere where I'm not known.'

'At last!' said Irena with a satisfied sigh 'now you're seeing sense!'

Jesus laughed. 'I must admit it will be quite a relief' he said 'we will go as far away as possible and we will pay our way and do our best not to get too close to people so that I can teach my disciples undisturbed.'

'You will have to harden your heart' said Mary looking anxious. 'If you only once heal somebody the crowds will come again.'

'I know Mary!' Jesus agreed 'I won't find it easy but after the summer is over perhaps we can find an isolated house to rent.'

'You're going to need money' interrupted Irena 'I'd better get hold of Joanna. She's started a fund, you know!'

'Yes I did know' said Jesus 'And I'm most grateful. We're going to need it now. I'd rather not rely on the goodness of men's hearts. People are too poor and I don't want to take advantage of them.'

'We already have enough money for a couple of months' said Irena. 'When it runs out you will have to send a message letting us know where you are so that one of us can come to you with more money.'

'I can do that' said James 'In the meantime can you sort out all the disciples and see that they all have the clothes and bedding they need? I think John needs a new cloak. His is not very warm!'

'We'll see to them, never fear!' Irena stood up looking purposeful 'And I'll see they are all bathed and shaved too!' She turned to Salome 'You can cut Andrew's hair. That boy never thinks about how he looks. If they're going from here then they can at least look respectable!'

Jesus gave her a quick hug. 'Thank you, all of you. I know you have a lot to do with the Sabbath starting tonight but you'll be able to rest a bit once we're gone!'

'I hope you are able to rest too' said Mary looking concerned 'Every day we've watched you getting more and more tired. You really need a break!'

'No crowds, no healing, just peace and quiet and healing of the soul. That is my intention.' Jesus went to the door 'We have to prepare ourselves for what is to come.' He turned and smiled once more. 'Without all your hard work my mission would have been very limited. You have made everything possible. When we are gone you too must rest and gird yourselves for hard days ahead.'

The women fell silent. They looked at each other in consternation. Mary was the first to speak 'Whatever happens' she said 'We will all be there for you. Right to the very end.'

I know!' said Jesus sadly 'You have all given for more than money or time. You have given your hearts, and the heart is always faithful.'

During the day Jesus sent his disciples to their homes to spend time with their families before the journey, but those who lived in Capernaum were soon together again at the morning Sabbath day service in the synagogue the next day.

The scribes and the Pharisees were there in force. A large phalanx of black robed men dominated the proceedings. Their responses were loud and pious and there was much lifting of hands in prayer and dramatic poses.

When Jesus walked in he and his disciples stayed back among the townsfolk and, seeing the great numbers of scribes, Jairus sensibly refrained from asking Jesus to read.

As the service proceeded several of the townsfolk surreptitiously edged towards Jesus to exchange a smile or touch his robe. The scribes, noticing this, scowled their disapproval from a distance, only to be met by defiant stares.

At the very back of the synagogue the new tax collector that had taken Matthew's place on the toll had slipped in and was keeping well hidden behind a pillar. He seemed distressed and lost in prayers of his own.

Matthew pointed him out to Jesus and as they all left the synagogue and emerged into the daylight Jesus reached out a hand and touched the tax collector's shoulder. The man turned and found himself looking directly into Jesus' eyes. Jesus smiled at him 'You have found favour with God' he said 'your sins are forgiven.'

Unable to move the man stood transfixed as Jesus looked deep into his eyes and then, with tears coursing down his cheeks, the man turned without a word and ran away.

Jesus turned to his disciples and to all those pressing around him. 'A Pharisee and a tax gatherer went to pray' he said and the Pharisee stood with his hands held high and thanked God that he was better than most people, more pious, more devout and certainly better than the vile tax gatherer who was hiding behind the pillar. The tax gatherer, on the other hand, was so ashamed of his sins he could barely bring himself to lift his head in God's house. "God be merciful to me" he cried silently "I am a sinner."'

Jesus lifted his voice 'And God was merciful!' he said 'That man had all his sins wiped clean. But the Pharisee, who could not see his own failings, still retains them.'

He looked around 'You must be careful' he said 'not to judge others. It would be like trying to take a speck of dust out of your neighbour's eye when you have a whole plank of wood in your own. First, you must be like the tax gatherer and recognise your own sins and ask for God's mercy. Then, like him, you will be blessed.'

A group of scribes emerging from the synagogue at that moment grabbed one of the men on the edge of the group listening to Jesus. 'What has he been saying?' they demanded.

The man laughed and shook off the hand that held him. 'He's telling us that we should all be more like tax collectors' he said and laughed again. 'You must admit his teaching is very different. I don't suppose you'll approve but what he says is down to earth and makes a lot of sense. I like it!'

The scribe snorted 'His type will always appeal to the ignorant' he sneered. 'He'll soon be found out as an ignorant charlatan himself!'

The man was already walking away but he couldn't resist a parting shot. 'You haven't bettered him yet though, have you? He's too clever for the likes of you!'

***

There was no breeze at all that day and the air in the little town grew hot and sultry. Unable to move far because of the Sabbath most people settled in the shade of walls and trees and dozed.

'Let's go out of the town a short way' suggested Jesus 'and leave the shady spots for the women.'

'We'd better be careful not to go beyond the limits' warned James. 'Those scribes from Jerusalem will be watching.'

'Simon must know where the limits lie. He can show us just where we can or cannot go' Jesus replied 'Come! We will find the air clearer outside of the town.'

It was more of an amble than a walk. The haze over the lake made it impossible to see the distant hills and in the increasing heat the song birds were silent. Keeping the buildings on their left and the farmer's fields' on their right they walked anti-clockwise around the town. They chattered quietly among themselves and when they reached the high point behind the town they sank down on the ground in the shade of a tree. They were only a few yards behind the synagogue and it was there that the group of scribes and Pharisees found them again.

Spoiling for a fight they were obviously disappointed that Jesus and his disciples had kept within the town limits as the Sabbath law required, but it didn't take them long to find fault. 'Have you seen what your disciples are doing?' one of them angrily demanded pointing at Andrew and young Simon. 'Look, they are working on the Sabbath! Why didn't you admonish them? As a teacher of the law it is your duty to make sure they keep the law.'

Everybody turned to look at the two young men who flushed and looked bewildered. 'Look, they are reaping!' insisted the scribe pointing angrily. And in the hands of the two young men were ears of corn that they had idly pulled from the farmer's field as they passed and, without thinking, were rolling in the palms of their hands to free the grain.

'And grinding!' said another of the scribes 'You must stop this blatant disobedience!'

The disciples dissolved into laughter and, after hastily dropping the corn and glancing anxiously at Jesus, Simon and Andrew sheepishly joined in.

The scribes stood their ground. There was no audience now but they were determined to have their way.

'Do you remember the story of King David?' asked Jesus calmly 'the greatest king Israel has ever known' he added. 'Do you remember the time when he was fleeing from Saul and he and his men were starving? What did he do?'

No-one replied.

Jesus continued 'He went to the sanctuary at Nob and went straight to Abiathar the high priest and he lied. He told Abiathar that he and his men were on the king's business and that he had been consecrated to perform a special mission, and he persuaded Abiathar to give him the consecrated bread from the altar to eat. And Abiathar gave it to him and when Saul found out he slaughtered Abiathar and all the priests of Nob for their complicity in helping David.'

Jesus looked around 'Our great King David lied, ate consecrated bread and caused the death of innocent priests and their families and yet he is revered and sanctified by us all.' He turned to the scribes and Pharisees 'And you are making a fuss about my disciples plucking ears of corn on the Sabbath! Don't you think, may be, that you are taking your criticism too far?'

'But David was anointed by God and was King' a Pharisee objected.

'David was a man' said Jesus firmly 'he had human failings and made mistakes, as will any son of David.'

'Are you saying that the Messiah when he comes will not be perfect?' demanded another.

'If he is a son of Man and, by birth, a son of David how can he help but be anything other than a sinner? However hard he tries he will always be human, subject to human desires and failings.'

The Pharisees were silent but the scribes turned to mutter among themselves. One of them turned accusingly 'It doesn't alter the fact that your disciples make no attempt to keep the law and you don't appear to be correcting them or teaching them what they should be doing.'

Jesus got to his feet and faced his accusers. There was sorrow in his voice. 'You sit in the chair of Moses and it is your task to guide the people towards God and the Kingdom of Heaven' he said. 'People look up to you and call you Rabbi or Father and you wear your phylacteries and your robes with long tassels. You are given places of honour at feasts and the chief seats in the synagogues and in return what do you do?'

His voice became angry. 'Your studying and your observance of the law has not brought you any closer to God and yet you insist that others must take that same path. If you see anyone, like my followers, coming close to the Kingdom by a different route you stop them.'

The group of scribes and Pharisees stared at him in amazement. They were not used to being criticised.

'You are blind guides, hypocrites! You make a fuss about the minutest details of the law, about tithing or washing or swearing and yet you ignore the most important law of all, the law of love. And what about justice, and mercy and good faith? It is these you should have practised, without neglecting the others. As it is you have made heavy packs to pile on men's shoulders and you do not raise a finger to help lift the burdens. You clean the outside of a cup and dish which you have already filled inside with evil thoughts and self indulgence. You must clean the inside of the cup first, and then the outside would also be clean.'

The scribe who had challenged Jesus when he had healed the paralysed man was flushed with rage. 'How dare you speak to us like this!' he shouted, barely able to speak the words he was so angry. 'We have given our lives to the law; you are a mere builder with no formal education. It is preposterous that you speak as you do.'

Jesus looked at him and when he spoke his voice was sad. 'When people look at you they see honest, pious men but they don't see beyond the trappings of your religion. You have become expert actors. On the outside you pretend to be faithful teachers of the word of God, but you are hypocrites! Don't you realise that you have made the traditions and the laws made by men like yourselves to be even more inportant than the true word of God?"

Speechless with anger the scribes stared at Jesus. In the silence that followed their eyes narrowed and hardened as his words sank in. Then, unable to find words of their own, they turned and walked away, their backs rigid with disapproval.

Jesus sat down again among his stunned disciples.

It was Nathaniel who broke the silence 'It's probably just as well we're going away tomorrow' he mused.

'That's the understatement of the year' exclaimed John making them all laugh.

Andrew handed John an ear of corn 'Here!' he said 'Have one!'

Jesus looked up with a wry smile 'I feel I must point out to you that you are breaking the law. That you have reaped and will now grind on the Sabbath. But,' he added and his smile grew wider 'if you have another one to hand Andrew, I would like one too!'

CHAPTER TWENTY

They left Galilee in the high summer. Leaving before the sun came up the people did not see them go and they were well on their way before the roads became busy with people and dusty in the heat.

Leaving the main road and cutting across country it wasn't long before they were on their own, and, as long as they kept to the tracks and the small hillside villages, they were undisturbed.

Jesus began to relax. He had time to talk to all of his disciples and to listen to their worries and to their hopes and their dreams. When they stopped moving about he would sit and talk to them and tell them stories and answer their questions. Most of all he encouraged them to pray. 'You must become men of prayer' he urged. 'Let God into your hearts and your lives will be always full of light and love. You will be transformed!'

'I am sending you out to be lights in a world of darkness' he reminded them. 'A woman doesn't light a candle to give light to her house and then put it under a bucket. In the same way' he continued 'you too will not be hidden. I am lighting each one of you with God's love and you will go out in the strength and power of this love to bring light to the world.'

The early autumn days that year were mild and for many weeks it was possible to sleep out at night around the embers of a campfire. They travelled further north into the territory of the Phoenicians and the Syrians. The hills were more spectacular and the trees tall and magnificent. The air was crisper and they all felt well rested and fit.

Only Simon seemed unhappy. 'He's missing his boat and the family' guessed Andrew but John wasn't so sure and several times saw Jesus and Simon deep in conversation. It was not like Simon to be so quiet.

Judas had charge of the money and as winter approached and the night air became colder he came to Jesus with a worried expression on his face. 'We have nearly used all the money' he said and, turning the bag out on the rock beside them allowed a few silver coins to tumble out. 'This is all we have left.'

'Are we going back then?' asked James.

'I hope not!' said John anxiously 'I feel I'm only just beginning to understand things. I'm not ready to go back to those crowds again!'

'Nor am I John' smiled Jesus 'we are none of us ready. We will stay here through the winter. I will get a message through to Irena and ask if Mary and Joanna can come here with some more money.' He looked at them all. 'We will spend a few more days sleeping rough and when the money comes we will find an empty house to rent for the winter. We can begin looking for one straight away.'

'If we stay in one place people will find us again' said Matthew.

'Not so many people travel in the winter' said Jesus 'and you, for one, need a more settled existence. I've seen you trying to keep your writing materials together. It's not easy when we're moving all the time to organise your notes.'

Matthew looked pleased 'And we'll be able to wash ourselves and our clothes more often' he added happily.

'And cut our hair!' agreed Andrew 'What joy!'

Mary and Joanna joined them a week later and helped them settle into an old house built on the edge of a forest of tall firs. They stayed a week and gave all the men messages from their families. They also cooked some tasty meals and organised the washing and drying of clothes. Jesus and the disciples were sorry to see them go but soon returned to their studies with enthusiasm.

Matthew was right in thinking that if they stayed in one place they would attract attention. They had only been in the house for six weeks when, on a visit to the local market a mile or so away, they were invited as a group to a meal in the house of a local dignitary.

Before they went there was much heating of hot water, shaving and washing. They had all been out of circulation for so long that they found they were nervous of socialising and it was a very quiet, anxious group that turned up at the large modern house built of cut limestone and framed by a strand of tall pines. The meal was delicious and after so long of cooking for themselves it was difficult for the disciples to eat at a polite and measured pace.

Their host seemed to know exactly who Jesus was and treated him with great deference and, realising that it was not necessary to keep their identity hidden, the young men began to relax.

When the meal finished the dishes were deftly removed from the low table and goblets of wine were efficiently replenished. It had been a most satisfactory and enjoyable evening.

It took a moment or two for them all to become aware of a disturbance by the servant's doorway. A large steward was remonstrating with one of the serving women. Ducking under his outstretched arms the woman broke loose and darted across the room to Jesus. The host hurried to prevent her reaching him but Jesus held up his hand. 'Let her come!' he said.

Falling on her knees at Jesus' side the woman cried 'Sir! Have pity on me! Son of David, I beg you to heal my daughter. She is possessed by a devil. Help me!'

The disciples were alarmed 'Send her away!' they begged Jesus. 'If you help her it will start all over again.'

Jesus looked at the woman with pity in his eyes. 'My mission is first and foremost to the lost souls among the people of Israel' he said.

'I know!' said the woman in misery 'But I don't ask for much. Just as the dogs under the table are eating up the crumbs from this meal so I am only asking for a tiny portion of your power. The children of Israel will lose nothing. Help me sir, please. Only say the word so that my child can be healed!'

Jesus smiled at her 'You have shown much love and great faith. It will be as you wish. Your daughter is healed!'

Stunned for a moment the woman was rooted to the spot. Then her face became wreathed with smiles and wonder. She scrambled to her feet and ignoring her master and the large steward she ran from the room and out of the house.

James looked at Jesus in dismay 'Why did you break our cover for that foreigner?' he asked 'She'll never be able to keep it quiet and we'll be surrounded by the crowds again.'

Jesus didn't speak for a moment 'I know James' he said 'but love knows no boundaries. The colour of the skin, different customs, different languages and nationalities; all these things separate us from one another, but love unites us all. That woman loved her child no more and no less than any Israelite woman. She loved enough to fight her corner. In my heart I didn't see a woman from Phoenicia or Syria I saw a woman who loved her child and I had to respond. The love of God will always respond to love.'

'It won't be long before the people find us, all the same' repeated James.

'We'll stay a few days longer and then we'll start our travels again' Jesus agreed. 'We've rested long enough and Matthew is nearly ready with his paper work in order.'

Nobody seemed to notice Simon slip from the room as they chatted politely to their hosts. He wasn't at the house when they returned but was there again for breakfast next day. Jesus just gave him a smile and a nod when he appeared and everything returned to normal.

When they resumed their travelling Jesus led them west back into Northern Israel towards Mount Hermon. At the foothills of the mountains stood Herod Philip's new town named for Caesar as Caesarea Philippi. 'Is this the Philip who was married to Herodias?' asked John.

'No!' said Matthew 'That Philip is an older man. He lives in Jerusalem, alone. This Philip is a younger son of Herod and Caesar gave him this northern portion to rule.

'Two sons with the same name!' exclaimed Andrew 'How stupid! And how confusing!'

'But not unusual' laughed Matthew 'Herod had several wives and they each chose the names they wanted. The scriptures tell us that King Solomon had seven hundred wives and three hundred concubines. If they all named their children I have no doubt there were many duplicate names!'

'King Herod was quiet abstemious in contrast then, wasn't he?' muttered Nathaniel making them all laugh.

'This is a beautiful city' said Thomas looking with a professional eye at the buildings. 'Sepphoris should look like this when it's finished, although its setting will not be as grand. That mountain makes a magnificent back drop.'

'We must give them their due' agreed Jesus 'The Herod family are very good for the building trade!' He began to stride ahead. 'Come and see the grotto. I don't think any of you have been here before and it's quite magnificent.'

Just outside the city the river Jordan gushed out of the side of the mountain. It bubbled up inside the mouth of a large cave and spilled over into a pool, and then turned into a fast moving stream and sped away south towards Galilee.

Inside the cave there was a white statue of the god Pan. 'That has been there a long time' said Jesus. 'The Greeks dedicated this grotto to Pan and the old town was named Bannias after him.'

'There are a lot of other statues of gods here now' said Nathaniel. 'I can count at least fourteen.'

Jesus smiled. 'You know what the Romans are like' he said 'they are so superstitious and they are so afraid of offending a god that they include them all.'

He looked around 'There is a vendor selling hot bread and figs to the tourists' he said 'let's use a little of our money and buy some food and sit here and eat it in the sun.'

Judas quickly rounded up the younger disciples and went off with the purse. Soon they had returned and leaning back against the boulders in the warm sun they all ate their meal in a companionable silence.

The meal ended Jesus got to his feet and looked down at the grotto. 'Who do people say I am?' he asked the young men.

Taken aback, they didn't reply immediately. 'Some say you're Elijah come back to live among us again' said James.

'Others think you're John the Baptist and that he didn't really die' said another.

'I've heard people say that you're Jeremiah' said John, but I can't think why!'

'That's because Jesus teaches about writing the law on our hearts and so did Jeremiah' said Matthew.

'Most agree that you are a prophet, a great prophet' they agreed.

Jesus was silent and then he turned and faced them. 'And you!' he said 'Who do you say that I am?'

There was an embarrassed silence. Then from the back of the group came Simon's deep voice 'You are the Messiah!' he said 'But not as foretold by the prophets. You are not merely the Son of Man, nor the Son of David.

You are the Son of the living God!'

The disciples gasped with astonishment, swivelling their heads to gaze at Simon.

'Well!' said Simon defiantly 'After all we've seen him do and heard him say, how can he be anything other than the Son of God?'

They all turned as a man back to Jesus.

Jesus was looking at his old friend with delight and amazement. 'Simon, son of Jonah,' he exclaimed 'you are favoured indeed. You didn't learn this from anyone but God himself. Of all people he has chosen to reveal the truth to you!'

Nobody spoke and then Jesus continued quietly looking directly at Simon. 'You are Peter, and on this rock, the rock of your faith and this understanding, I will build my church. The love of God will grow because of you and the powers of death will never conquer it. You Peter will hold the keys to the Kingdom of Heaven and because you have shown a wisdom that is beyond human understanding you will open the doors of the Kingdom to allow my people in.'

Jesus sat down once again and continued. 'Now this moment has come. Now all my teaching has led us to this point' he said. 'We are now ready to take the message to Jerusalem.'

The disciples exchanged excited glances, but Jesus was quick to put them right. 'This will not be an easy journey as the one we have just known. The way ahead will be hard' he said grimly. 'Opposition has already begun and will quickly grow. This opposition will lead to my death.'

Peter got to his feet and rushed forward 'No!' he cried 'No Lord! This must not happen to you!'

Jesus turned on him sternly 'Get behind me Satan; you are a stumbling block to me. Now you are thinking as a man and forgetting that it is what God wants that matters!'

Peter looked ready to burst into tears and Jesus put out his hand to his old friend. 'Peter' he said sadly 'it is your love and your friendship that can undo me when I desperately need to be strong. If I was harsh it was because the devil is at last realising where my weakness lies. But remember all of you' he said looking around at the frightened faces of his followers 'the powers of death can never conquer the power of love. I must die, but I will rise again after three days. Keep this in mind and be strong. Don't worry about your own safety. Take up your cross and follow me. God will be with you and his holy angels will minister to you. No harm will come to you.'

The disciples sat rigid with fear and bewilderment. 'Do not be afraid' urged Jesus 'in simple terms it means that I will be with you, even unto the end of the world. But now!' his voice was urgent 'Don't speak of any of this to anyone. It is too much for others to understand. This must be our secret.'

CHAPTER TWENTY ONE

It was night when they returned to Capernaum. No one saw them arrive and the men went quietly to their homes. Without lighting a lamp Simon Peter stepped silently through the darkened rooms of his house and slipped thankfully under the covers of his bed. Reaching for the soft, rounded form of his beloved wife he let out a long sigh of relief and contentment.

Still drowsy with sleep Sarah murmured and began to wake, her eyes opening wide in surprise as Simon, reaching over quickly, smothered her mouth with kisses. Still clinging to each other Sarah whispered at last 'How long are you staying? Where is Jesus?'

'Everyone except Jesus has gone home' Simon replied with a chuckle. 'The last time I saw him he was walking along the shore towards Bethsaida. He's gone to pray!'

Instantly anxious Sarah sat up 'When is he going to sleep?' she demanded.

'Prayer seems to refresh him more than sleep' said Simon reaching for her again 'Come here and relax!' he urged 'We have only a short time and then we are going south.'

'To Jerusalem?'

'I don't think so!' Simon replied 'At least not immediately. But Jesus did say something about all of you joining us in Jerusalem for Passover.'

'That's two months away' she whispered as she settled down again and drew Simon towards her. 'It's hard being without you' she mused 'I hadn't realised what it would be like. We can manage the business and the children but I've really missed you, my husband.'

'You don't regret my going with Jesus, do you?' Simon asked anxiously.

'No! It is the right thing. He needs you!' she was adamant. 'But I need you too!' she added with a giggle. 'Don't let's waste a moment!'

When they woke the next morning they found Jesus sitting on the bench overlooking the lake. The air was cool and the water was grey and choppy. Jesus did indeed look rested and as Sarah and Irena came out of the house he stood up and walked towards them with a smile of affection.

'It's so good to see you both again' he said 'I've missed you! Indeed we've all missed you!'

'My cooking more like!' snorted Irena. But she looked pleased all the same.

'Speaking of which' began Jesus and they all laughed.

'Alright, alright!' nodded Irena happily 'Be patient I'll have some food ready in a moment!' She shivered and drew her shawl around her 'don't stay out here in the cold. Come in to the house and warm up!' Looking around at the sleeping town she said 'Thankfully the weather is still cold or the neighbours would have been outside by now and you would have been seen. Come on now! Get inside!'

**

Jesus seemed anxious to leave again within days. There was a new determination and intensity about him and his disciples responded by gathering together again and preparing themselves for a further journey without questions or delay.

It was decided that Mary and Salome, the mother of James and John, would travel with them and that other family members, including Jesus' mother, would meet them in Jericho in two months time so that with all the Galilean pilgrims they could make the ascent to Jerusalem together for the Passover.

The weather was still cold when they left Capernaum and John was glad of his thicker cloak. Even so he wrapped it tightly around him as they skirted the lake and began the long walk south.

When they reached the first of the new houses on the edge of Herod's new Tiberias they took the road inland for a while before joining the main road again once they were clear of the town. Herod had taken no notice of his advisers when they had warned him that this land, although uniquely positioned over the natural hot springs was also the site of an ancient graveyard. Intent on honouring the Emperor Tiberius Herod had gone ahead with the building of an elegant Roman style city and had made a wonderful and unforgettable feature of the hot baths. He built his own palace there and hosted Roman officers and guests from Caesarea and even from as far away as Rome but the Jews shunned the town and it was virtually impossible to find tradesmen or servants who were prepared to work there. Indeed it was easier to get them to visit Macherus, way out in the desert, rather than this elegant Galilean town.

A few miles further south again Jesus led his disciples off the main road and on to a track that began to rise steadily. Ahead of them a rounded, flat topped hill rose out of the plain. It stood alone and as they drew closer they could see its steep sides were criss-crossed with sheep paths.

Gathering his disciples around him Jesus pointed to the hill 'This is where Deborah defeated the armies of Sisera' he said. 'Look how it rises out of the plan. To the north lies Galilee and to the south are the hills of Samaria and beyond them Jerusalem itself.' He turned to Simon 'I want to climb to the top' he said 'Will you and James and John come with me?'

'Of course!' agreed Simon 'After all the walking we've done over the last few weeks I've never been fitter.'

John looked at the hill 'Count me in!' he said 'Although my older brother may have a problem!'

Jesus laughed and looked at James who caught his eye and nodded with a smile. Turning to Judas Jesus continued 'While we are gone can you find lodgings and food for everyone in that village? It's too cold to sleep out at night.'

Judas patted the purse hanging from his belt 'Joanna and her friends have been most generous' he said 'We should be alright for a few months now.'

'That's good!' Jesus agreed 'I don't know how long we will be but we'll find you in the village when we come down.'

The disciples and the two women moved off towards the small huddle of houses at the foot of the hill and Jesus, with Simon James and John strode purposefully towards the nearest of the sheep paths.

'It'll be just our luck if this path comes to a dead end or twists back down again' laughed John.

'We can easily find another' said James 'the whole hillside is criss-crossed by them. At least there's not a great deal of vegetation and we can see our way.'

'As long as we keep going up!' added Simon stepping around a boulder on the path.

'Going up but looking down!' said John rubbing his ankle 'this path is quite treacherous and the stones have sharp edges!'

'It's as well we have our bed rolls with us' said Jesus 'you're right John it could be dangerous trying to come down again in the half light. I think we should stay up the hill tonight and come down again in the morning1'

Puffing a little from the exertion of climbing Simon pointed to a sharp drop on the side of the path ahead. 'Daylight seems a good idea to me!' he grunted. 'A drop like that would be the end of us all.'

It took them nearly two hours of climbing to reach the top and, gasping for breath, they looked in awe at the view. It was possible to look in all directions and see the fields in the valley below with the green hills of Galilee to the north and the brown hills of Samaria to the south. Whichever way they turned they could see for miles and looking to the west the grey clouds lifted enough for them to see the sun, very low in the sky, throw out its golden rays and light up the horizon.

Reaching for the water skins that hung over their shoulders, the men sank down on the flat boulders and drank deeply. There was a chill in the wind but they were still hot from the exertion of climbing. It was a good feeling and when John produced a smaller, second skin from around his waist and announced that he had taken the precaution of bringing some wine with him for medicinal purposes, they all collapsed with laughter.

They ate the bread and figs that each was carrying and they shared the wine as they watched the sun go down. And as darkness fell they began to feel the cold. It wasn't long before the disciples had wrapped themselves in their bedding and each had found a place behind a boulder and out of the wind to sleep.

Jesus wrapped his blanket around himself and walked a little way away. 'I have come here to pray' he said to them all 'the time is very near and I need to ask my Father for help.' He looked into their eyes, one by one 'I'm glad you're here with me' he said 'It is a difficult time and I need my friends.'

Not quite knowing what to say the three men flushed with pride and watched him with affection as he walked away and stood alone in prayer. 'I'll follow him to the ends of the earth!' thought each man as he settled down to keep watch over his beloved master. 'I'll never let him down!' and then each man closed his eyes and slept.

It was daylight when they woke and a low cloud hung over the summit of the mountain. It must have been sunny elsewhere because the cloud was diaphanous with light.

Simon struggled to his feet, unsure for a moment where he was. Then he remembered and swung round looking for Jesus. 'I didn't intend to go to sleep' he muttered to himself, 'not when he so obviously needed us.' And then he stood stock still. Ahead of him, enveloped by the cloud, stood Jesus. The sun streaming through the cloud picked out the white of his tunic and he was surrounded by the light. The skin of his face appeared luminous. Dazzled for a moment Simon shielded his eyes and just then became aware that James and John were by his side and that they too were gazing in awe at Jesus.

'What's happening?' whispered John, rubbing his eyes but neither Simon nor James replied. 'Who is he talking to?' John insisted, and he stared into the cloud.

Beside Jesus in the moving white cloud were two figures and all three were all talking earnestly. James caught John's arm 'Look at that old man!' he whispered 'could that be Moses himself? And the other one, dressed in skins, is that Elijah?'

'How could it be?' John whispered back 'It's not possible!'

'Don't you understand?' demanded Simon excitedly 'Everything and anything is possible. I'm not surprised by anything any more!'

'They're leaving!' whispered James and as they watched the two figures stepped back into the cloud and disappeared.

Simon sprang forward to Jesus. 'Master!' he cried 'What a wonderful thing. We've actually seen Moses and Elijah! Their feet have touched this very spot!' and he pointed with reverence to the ground in front of him.

'This is hallowed ground!' he exclaimed 'Let us build booths around this spot. One for Moses and one for Elijah and one for you!'

As he spoke the cloud around the mountain top grew darker and closed in, swirling about the men. Suddenly a voice was heard by them all.

'This is my Son, my beloved. Listen to him!'

Simon fell on the ground in fear and James and John clung to each other. Jesus stood alone surrounded by light.

Looking up at him in wonder the three men were suddenly overcome with feelings of shame and inadequacy. Closing their eyes to shut out the light they dropped their heads unable to speak, unable to move and hardly able to breathe.

When they opened their eyes the cloud was gone and Jesus was alone. As he walked towards them they all sank to their knees and he reached out to each of them. 'Get up!' he said 'Don't be afraid!' Then looking at their frightened faces he asked anxiously 'Did you hear the voice that time?'

Unable to speak they nodded and looked up at Jesus with bewilderment in their eyes. Jesus looked relieved. Again he reached out his hands and helped the disciples to their feet. 'Come!' he said 'It's time to go!'

Gathering up their belongings they scrambled after him down the hillside. No one spoke for a while but then Jesus stopped and looking up at the three men said 'Tell no one what you have seen and heard today! Keep it a secret until after my death!'

'Your death Lord?' questioned John in a whisper.

'Yes John! It will happen and soon' replied Jesus sadly and then continued 'The prophecy said that Elijah would come to herald the Messiah and so he has and they have killed him!'

'Do you mean John, the baptiser?' asked James 'Every time I looked at him he reminded me of the prophet Elijah.'

'Yes James I do' Jesus continued 'and now he is dead and it won't be long before I am too. But first!' he said 'I have more to teach you all.'

He looked south towards the brown hills of Samaria 'We will go through Samaria and then down beyond Jericho to the desert where John was baptising and we will stay there for a few weeks in the warmer climate and I can prepare you all for what is to come.'

He turned back to the track. 'Let's go!' he said.

'We're going back to the desert?' questioned John in alarm.

'Yes John!' Jesus replied 'I have my devils to fight and decisions to make and the desert is a good place to do both.'

John's face grew pale with worry. Neither Simon nor James had seen Jesus when he had last come from the desert so it was no use talking to them. He needed Andrew.

As it was it was Andrew that came hurrying out to meet them as they approached the village. 'I knew you would come back this morning!' he exclaimed 'There is a young man possessed of a devil that is so powerful none of us can get rid of it!' He paused for breath. 'We've all tried and we've all failed! Thank goodness you are here!'

Jesus was stern 'What has happened to you all? Where is your faith?' he demanded. 'Bring the boy to me!'

Taken aback by Jesus' tone of voice Andrew rushed in to the house. The disciples spilled out on to the road followed by the young lad and his parents. The boy seemed calm and was walking steadily. Seeing Jesus, his father stepped quickly forward 'Teacher!' he cried 'I beg you help my son. He is my only child but all of a sudden a spirit will seize him and throw him to the floor and he has convulsions and foams at the mouth. It doesn't last long but it keeps happening and my poor son has no strength left to fight it.'

As he spoke the boy, gazing with fear at Jesus, tore himself away from his mother and fell violently on to the ground. His arms thrashed wildly. He lay there jerking uncontrollably. The disciples stepped back in alarm and the boy's mother ran forward and cradled her son's head as he thrashed around. She desperately tried to stop him hurting himself still more on the rough path and tears coursed down her cheeks as her husband stood helplessly by.

Jesus' eyes softened with compassion as he watched the mother and stepping right up to where the child lay he spoke with a voice that seemed to call far into the soul. 'Come out of him!' he ordered and he leant forward and touched the child's head. 'Be still!' he said quietly 'Be still! All will be well!' Suddenly the thrashing stopped and the child lay still and Jesus looked at the anxious parents 'Your son is well again. You do not need to worry!'

Andrew interrupted anxiously 'How is it that we couldn't heal him? We all tried!'

'I know Andrew' said Jesus sorrowfully 'This kind of healing can only come about through prayer!'

Nathaniel spoke up 'That's our weakest point' he said anxiously 'we still have a lot to learn.'

'Yes!' agreed Jesus 'And there is so little time left!'

'But we're going down to the desert' said John gloomily 'It's scary enough to get all of us praying1'

'The desert?' queried Andrew anxiously looking at Jesus.

'Yes Andrew' said Jesus with a smile. 'John's right. It is a good place to learn to pray. We'll go down through Samaria tomorrow!'

When John groaned Jesus grinned 'Personally' he said 'I can't wait!'

CHAPTER TWENTY TWO

As they took the road through the Samarian uplands the disciples speculated excitedly about the moment when Jesus would reveal himself in Jerusalem. He was surely so popular now that no one would oppose him. They all agreed he was the Messiah. The people would make him king. The whole world would know about him and them. After all they were his chosen few, his friends. With every stop they took their excitement mounted.

Seemingly oblivious to the speculations of his followers Jesus strode out ahead of them, alone. His face was set with a grim determination and his pace never faltered.

Running to catch with up him Salome slipped away from the others and when she came close she reached out and caught his arm. 'Jesus!' she exclaimed breathlessly.

Jesus stopped walking and looked down at his aunt with a smile. 'Yes Salome' he said 'what is the matter?'

Salome caught her breath and then the words came tumbling out. 'When you come in to your Kingdom Jesus, will you give my boys a special honour? Can they sit on your right and on your left?'

Jesus looked distressed 'My dear aunt!' he said with a sigh 'You don't know what it is you are asking.'

Catching up with Jesus and Salome the others gathered anxiously round, wondering what had caused Jesus to look so sad. Jesus looked at John and James. 'Are you able to share with me all that is to come? Can you drink from the cup that I will drink from and be baptised with the tribulation that I shall be baptised with?'

Looking bewildered John and James nodded their heads vigorously 'Yes Lord we can!' they both agreed. The disciples exchanged glances.

Jesus looked sadly at his cousins. 'You will indeed drink from the cup that I will drink from and be baptised with the baptism that I too will experience. But' he said firmly 'to sit at my right hand and at my left hand that I cannot promise. It is not mine to grant. These places have already been reserved by my father for those he has prepared.'

The other disciples began to look indignant. 'Sit at his right and left hand?' they questioned James and John. 'Why you? What makes you so special?'

John flushed deeply and Jesus intervened before an argument could arise. 'Look' he said pointing ahead of him down the road to the south. 'Look! We are taking the road to Jerusalem and, rather than being honoured, I will instead be arrested, condemned and killed.' He looked at Salome 'You surely can't be asking for your sons to be sharing that!' he said. Salome's face grew pale.

'Remember!' Jesus continued 'Mine is not an earthly Kingdom. In the Kingdom of Heaven the values of this world are turned on their head. It is the servant, the slave and the child that will hold the places of honour in my Kingdom. Whoever wants to be great in my Kingdom must be a slave to all he meets. Like me!' he went on 'I am among you as a servant and I have come to lay down my life in order that you may live.'

The disciples were silent, suddenly very afraid. Jesus smiled and in a gentler tone explained 'The Messiah must die' he said 'but never fear' he continued 'after three days

I will rise again and then you will know without doubt that you need never be afraid again.'

'Rise again?' whispered Andrew to Simon 'From the dead, does he mean?'

Simon groaned 'I can't take it all in' he whispered back 'It's all too much but, yes, I suppose if the chazzan's daughter and that boy in Nain can come back from the dead then Jesus can too!'

Andrew shook his head 'Perhaps that's not what he meant' he mused.

Jesus gathered them to him again. 'There's a village a little way ahead' he said 'John and James, go ahead of us all and see if you can arrange beds and food!'

Thankful to be doing something that took them away from their friends for a while the two brothers sprinted off and the others walked more slowly down the road with James in their midst.

As they drew closer to the village John and James suddenly emerged from between the first cluster of houses. Their faces were dark with anger. 'They don't want to know!' said John furiously 'They say we're just using their country as a corridor!'

James was also angry 'They were so rude!' he muttered 'Their language was appalling.'

Jesus laughed at their indignation and John exploded. 'Don't laugh!' he shouted 'How dare they treat you like this! Use your power and bring down a thunderbolt to consume the village! That's what they deserve!'

Jesus laughed again 'Boanarges!' he exclaimed 'Sons of Thunder. That's a good name for you both!'

Seeing their indignation he went forward and put his arms across their shoulders. 'Come on!' he said 'Don't be upset. There are many more villages. We will stop here by the road for a while and rest and then we'll move on. We'll have a bed tonight, never fear!'

Leaning into Jesus' shoulder the two men relaxed and then with a rueful grin John looked up 'Boanarges!' he repeated 'Yes! I like that!' He pulled himself up and puffed out his chest making them all laugh. 'A man to be reckoned with!' he declared glaring around at them all.

Simon punched him on the top of his arm 'You can see just how scared we all are' he laughed. 'Why!' he declared 'Judas is shivering in his shoes!'

They all turned to look at Judas who was doubled up and shaking with mirth and they all collapsed with laughter.

It felt strange to be laughing when Jesus had so recently been speaking of his death but it eased the tension and drew them all closer together. Of course there would be another village where they could stay.

They did find somewhere to sleep but it was already dark and getting quite cold when a householder agreed to let them use his barn. The following day things were not much better and they quickened their pace to make sure they were out of Samaria before the next evening came.

As they walked they suffered name calling and insults from small groups of Samaritans. It was a great relief to them all when they finally crossed over the border into Judea and made their way through the desert hill towards Jericho, the Jordan and the desert beyond.

They all felt indignant and ill used and were glad when Jesus began to tell them one of his stories. They moved closer to him as they walked so that they could hear more clearly and the desert hills around them became grey and menacing as the sun sank in the west. A few miles ahead lay the inn where they would stay for the night.

'Once upon a time' said Jesus 'there was a man who travelled this road from Jerusalem to Jericho. It was evening and bandits lay waiting for him and when the time was right they pounced, and beating him up, stole everything he had.'

The disciples glanced uneasily at the cliffs and the deepening shadows.

'They left him for dead at the side of the road' continued Jesus 'and by chance a priest walked down the road. He saw the body and quickly stepped to the other side of the road and hurried on! Then' said Jesus, 'a Levite also came along, and he did the same and the poor man was left, unconscious and close to death.'

He paused and then said 'The next person who passed this way was a Samaritan. He got off his donkey and went over to the man and, finding him still alive, he picked him up and put him on the back of the beast and walked him slowly down to the inn. He rented a room for the man and spent the night tending his wounds. In the morning he gave the inn keeper money to care for him until he was well enough to travel again.'

'Now!' Jesus' voice was challenging 'Which of those three was a true neighbour to the man who was attacked?'

There was an ashamed silence and no one would venture an answer. It was Mary who broke the silence 'It was the one who showed mercy' she said quietly.

'Say it Mary!' said Jesus with a smile.

'It was the Samaritan!' she answered 'And you're trying to tell us that they're not all bad!'

'I am!' agreed Jesus 'And you know something more? The priest and the Levite were probably good men too but their religion got in the way. They had come from Jerusalem where they had offered sacrifices and preformed their religious duties and were ritually clean. If they had touched the man they would have become ritually unclean. So they walked by on the other side of the road!'

'But the Samaritan had no such rules and regulations!' said Mary 'And so was free to follow his heart!' She paused 'Does that mean that religions are wrong?'

'No Mary!' Jesus' voice was heavy 'But a religion that does not make room for compassion and love but instead promotes pride and piousness is not from God. God is love and those who abide in love abide in God.'

'A good Samaritan!' grunted John with a chuckle 'Whatever next!'

'And what's more a Samaritan with a heart!' echoed James 'and not a thunderbolt in sight!' They all laughed.

A small light appeared on the road ahead 'Look!' said Andrew thankfully 'We're nearly there. I, for one, will be glad to get off this scary road and into a warm bed!'

The next morning they had reached the escarpment wall and below them they could see Herod's winter palaces. The water in the swimming pool where Queen

Marianne's young brother was murdered by Herod the Great's courtiers, glinted in the sun and looked blue and inviting. Beyond the palaces lay the green branches of the date palms that hid the ancient town of Jericho.

They bought food and vegetables from the street vendors and, piled high with their purchases, they walked on down to the Jordan crossing and the desert land beyond. The air was dry and warm and they felt their spirits rising.

'We'll stay here until winter is over' said Jesus 'We'll stay here and allow the warmth of God's love to fill our souls so that we are ready for all that is to come.' He looked at them all 'This is our last training camp' he said 'this is where we pray!'

CHAPTER TWENTY THREE

Time stood still. The caves where they made their camp were cool in the heat of the day but around the campfire built in the middle of the floor at night they felt safe and warm.

Jesus talked to them all both individually and together. He walked with them and prayed with them and little by little they learnt about a heavenly father who loved them. They learnt just how unique and precious they each were in God's eyes. 'Let God who loves you enter your hearts' he said to them. 'Talk to him. Get to know him. Allow him to know you. Talk to him like a friend. He will never leave you!'

'Did you think that you chose to follow me? If so you are deluded. It was my heavenly father who chose you. Each of you is unique. Each of you has a mission.'

'We've given up everything to follow you' said Simon anxiously.

'Yes Simon, I know and my heavenly father knows too. All that you have given up in this life will be rewarded to you a hundred fold in my Kingdom. Never fear! My father who sees in secret will reward in secret too.'

The desert itself was harsh. The stones were sharp and cut their feet and the wind rasped at their skin like sand paper but as the days passed they gradually lost their fear of the wide open spaces. Day by day they each walked further and further into the desert alone.

'Nothing is impossible to you if you have the love of God in your heart' Jesus told them.

Occasionally it rained, causing torrents of water to career down the steep valleys before sinking without trace into the loose stones of the valley floor. But most days the sun was hot even though the wind was often cold.

Standing on a ridge with the desert hills stretching all around them they looked in awe at the emptiness of their surroundings. The wind was fierce that day and Jesus had to raise his voice to be heard.

'Feel the wind' he said 'it blows where it wills. It is so strong the noise of it can be deafening. You can hear it and feel it, and you can see what it can do. But where does it come from and where is it going?'

He looked at their puzzled faces. 'So it is with the Spirit of God' he continued 'If the Spirit of God is born in your hearts you will know it. You will feel it and you will see what wonders it can do.'

He beckoned them over into the lee of the rocks where the wind was less fierce. 'When I am gone' he continued 'I will not leave you comfortless. My spirit, the Holy Spirit of God, will come upon you and fill your hearts. You will feel it and you will know it, and when it enters your hearts you will be fearless and full of joy for you will know that I am with you. So do not be afraid for I shall be with you even unto the end of the world!'

'When will that happen?' demanded John 'How will we know the Spirit has come?'

Jesus looked into his eyes with affection and laughed. 'You will know' he said with a nod of certainty 'You will feel it happen just as you feel the power of this desert wind. As for when it will happen I can't answer you yet. First I must die!'

John's eyes registered his shock 'I didn't mean...' he began.

'I know John!' said Jesus 'But it's true! My spirit must be freed by death before it can enter into the hearts of those who love me.' He paused and looked at them all 'It will not be long now!'

It was a very sober group that returned to the caves. There two men, dressed in smart city clothes were awaiting their arrival. Their faces were anxious and they approached Jesus with great reverence. 'Master!' they said bowing their heads. 'Master! Your friend Lazarus of Bethany is sick and his sisters beg you to come to him.'

Looking concerned Jesus questioned the men closely and then seemed to make up his mind. 'This illness will not lead to death' he concluded. 'I will come, but not today!' He looked at the men. 'You're tired. Stay and eat with us and sleep here tonight and then you can return tomorrow and tell Mary and Martha that I will come in a few days!'

The men looked anxious. 'Master!' said one 'He is indeed very ill. His sisters are very worried!'

'Yes I know!' said Jesus calmly in a tone that seemed to silence further questioning 'I will go in a few days' he repeated.

The men returned to Bethany the next day but Jesus had disappeared during the night and didn't see them go. He stayed alone in the desert returning only early on the fourth morning. Walking briskly back into the camp, he looked purposeful and determined.

'Lazarus, my friend has fallen asleep and it is time now to wake him up!' he said leaning down to pick up his bed roll.

The disciples looked puzzled. 'How do you know he's asleep?' demanded Andrew.

'Surely if he's sleeping that's a good thing isn't it?' said John. 'It means he's on the mend!'

'No John. I meant that Lazarus is dead. I'm going to him now!'

'You're not going alone' protested Thomas 'It's too dangerous! We'll come with you!'

'Yes! I want you all to come' agreed Jesus 'I have delayed on purpose so that you can witness the great power of the Spirit. Come. We must hurry!'

He picked up his water skin and plunged it in a bucket of clean water watching it while it filled. Then he put the stopper in place and, shaking off the water drops, swung it over his shoulder and made to stride out of the camp.

The disciples scrambled to gather their belongings and ran to catch him up. John caught Andrew's arm. 'We've been here before!' he grinned.

'Yes!' agreed Andrew 'And it's still just as scary!'

***

They climbed the road that zigzagged up the escarpment and reached the plateau in only a few hours. In fact the whole journey was shorter than any of them could remember it being before. Jesus seemed deep in thought and strode ahead, and the disciples followed, almost running in their anxiety to keep up.

It was late afternoon when they turned off the road towards Bethany. The narrow road was busy with people. Workers returning from the city stood on street corners sharing the latest news before disappearing into their homes. Local women leant against the door posts of their houses while children played in the street.

As Jesus reached the outskirts of the village one of the villagers recognised him instantly and turned on his heels and ran ahead to find Martha. 'He's come!' he said 'The miracle worker has arrived!' and gathering up her skirts Martha left everything and ran. The mourners were still in the house and Mary was with them but Martha left them all without a word and fled down the street flinging herself into Jesus' arms.

'Lord if you had been here' she gasped 'my brother would not have died!'

Jesus looked distressed.

'But you could still do something I know you can!' she continued 'If you ask God he will deny you nothing.'

Holding her at arm's length Jesus looked into her eyes 'Your brother will rise again' he said.

Martha gulped 'Yes Lord I know he will rise again in the resurrection at the last day.'

'No Martha!' said Jesus gently 'Listen to me carefully. I am the resurrection and the life, he who believes in me, though he die, yet shall he live, and whoever lives and believes in me shall never die. Do you believe this?'

Martha did not hesitate. 'Yes Lord!' she replied 'I know you are the Anointed One. I know you are the Son of God.'

'Send for Mary' said Jesus 'and take me to Lazarus' tomb.'

Martha reached out to the servant that had followed her 'Bring Mary!' she said 'But do it quietly. Don't bring all the mourners.'

The servant sped away and Jesus and the disciples walked slowly after Martha as she led the way towards the tombs.

Within minutes Mary come running down the road, her face drawn and ravaged from weeping. Following her at a more dignified pace were Lazarus' friends. When she reached Jesus she threw herself on the ground in her distress, weeping openly. 'Jesus!' she cried 'If only you had come then my beautiful, sensitive brother would not have died.'

Jesus stood still, deeply moved by her tears. He looked around. The quiet, dignified young Lazarus had many friends and all were stunned by his death and many were openly crying.

Tears appeared in Jesus' eyes. One of the bystanders nudged his fellow. 'He must have loved Lazarus very much.'

'Not enough to get here in time to prevent him dying' replied the other with a shrug.

Ignoring the crowd Jesus leant down and drew Mary to her feet. 'Show me where you have laid him' he said and following the two women he walked out of the village to the tombs cut in to the hillside.

When they reached the cave a stone had been rolled across the entrance. 'Take away the stone' ordered Jesus to his disciples and Thomas and Andrew ran to do his bidding.

Martha protested 'But Jesus!' she cried 'He's been dead for four days. There will be a terrible smell!'

'Don't distress yourself Martha' Jesus replied 'remember what I told you would happen to those who believe?'

She nodded mutely.

The dark entrance to the cave yawned open and Jesus took a pace forward pulling his shawl over his head. Lifting his voice and his hands in prayer, he spoke 'My Father. Thank you for listening to my voice. You are always with me and you always listen to me but for the sake of all these people who loved your servant Lazarus I ask you to show them now how love can triumph over everything, even death itself.'

And he stood and cried with a loud voice 'Lazarus. Come out!'

His voice echoed around the cave and the crowd was silent. The silence seemed to last for ever and then suddenly a sigh of relief and amazement caught in everyone's throat. A movement from inside the dark tomb was seen clearly by all present and, slowly, falteringly, the slim figure of Lazarus was seen moving towards the entrance. His grave clothes still wrapped around his body were unravelling from his arms and legs as he walked. The cloth that had covered his face lay on the earth floor behind him and the crowd gasped again as they gazed in fascinated horror at the pale, luminous face of the friend they had known and loved, and who they had so recently seen dead.

Lazarus stepped into the sunlight and blinked. He looked at everyone in bewilderment and then he saw Jesus with Mary and Martha beside him. Tears were streaming down their faces. Tears of joy!

Lazarus tugged at the bindings on his legs and, leaving them flapping behind him, he stumbled across the ground that separated them. His face was wreathed with smiles and he flung his arms around them all and the four of them stood together surrounded by their love and their thankfulness, alone in the middle of the amazed crowd.

An eruption of noise and speculation swirled around. 'Had he really been dead? Was it a trick? Who was this Jesus? What had really happened here?'

Leaving the noisy crowd, Jesus, with Lazarus, his sisters and the disciples moved discreetly back into the house and the gates were firmly locked.

The scribes and the Pharisees in the crowd hurriedly gathered together to discuss what they had seen. 'He was dead' said one of the Pharisees. 'I oversaw the laying out. He was definitely not faking.'

'Our colleagues in Galilee have sent reports of this fellow's teaching and a vast number of different healing miracles but this is something very different.' The scribes were non plussed 'What are we supposed to think?'

'If it's a trick it's a very clever one' said another 'the whole of Jerusalem will hear of this and there could be no stopping him. I think the Chief Priests should be told immediately.'

'Better they hear it from us' said one of the Pharisees anxiously 'Caiaphas will not be happy if it comes to him through gossip or rumour mongering.'

Standing quietly at the back of the group one of the elders voiced a note of caution. 'I believe we have witnessed something quite amazing' he said slowly 'and if that is so then this Jesus is a most remarkable man, a prophet at least!'

'Surely the High Priests must make that decision!' protested another. If this man is a trickster and a charlatan we'd be made to look such fools. The quicker we alert Annas and Caiaphas the better!'

In the end it was decided that three of the younger Pharisees would go back into the city and try and seek an audience with Caiaphas, for, after all, it was he and not his domineering father in law Annas who was the real High Priest. But they went with much trepidation. They didn't imagine that Caiaphas would thank them for interrupting his evening nor for delivering such disturbing news.

And they were right. Caiaphas' face was grim when they finished their tale. 'I want you back here tomorrow morning by the third hour' he ordered. 'You will repeat what you have told me to the whole Council!' and his cloak swirled behind him as he turned and stalked back in to his house.

The servants ushered them back through the courtyard and before they had realised what had happened they were outside in the darkened street and the metal gates had been closed behind them.

The following morning it was obvious that Caiaphas had not wasted any time in finding out the facts. His spies must have spent a busy night. All the reports of Jesus' actions in Galilee had been gathered. Details of his family were known and each of the disciples had a file all to themselves.

'He's a danger!' Old Annas was determined to control the meeting and his face was already red with fury. Not everyone agreed. Nicodemus got to his feet 'He is clever and articulate and I believe him to be a man of God, a prophet, perhaps the greatest prophet we have ever known' he said firmly 'we should listen to what he has to say.'

'Listen to him? Are you mad?' Annas jumped to his feet 'In two week's time over a million pilgrims will be here for Passover. If this man causes even the slightest disturbance the Romans will not allow the feast to continue. And you know what that will mean1'

'Yes!' said Nicodemus calmly 'You priests will make no money this year1'

'How dare you!' blustered Annas 'Anyone would think you were a disciple of this wretched man.'

'I am an old man now' said Nicodemus sadly 'you can't frighten me with your bullying any more and yes I do believe I am a follower of this young man. I believe we ignore him at our peril!'

'But if we allow him free reign and the people take up his cause we could lose control altogether!' another Council member was anxious.

'It would help if we know where he is and what he is doing at all times' said Caiaphas' secretary 'if we could get one of his followers to keep us informed we could keep a close watch and perhaps prevent any problems.'

'His followers are all ignorant fishermen and builders!' scoffed an elderly Council member.

'Not all' interrupted another. 'Two of them at least are members of the Zealot party.'

'Still ignorant then!' grunted the elder.

'We'll try those two first' agreed the secretary ignoring the banter. He looked at the notes. 'One is named Simon, the other Judas. I'll get on to it!'

'It's still too dangerous!' protested Annas 'We should just get rid of him!'

'The crowds will object. We could have more trouble than we can manage' another Council member got to his feet and, encouraged by the nodding heads of the members around him he continued 'and what if he really is a prophet?'

Caiaphas, who had been quiet until this moment, got to his feet forcing the speaker to sit down. 'We will watch this man carefully!' he said firmly. 'Everything he does and everything he says will be reported to me' his eyes were cold as he looked around at the Council 'I will particularly want to know when and where this Jesus goes when he leaves the city. I want to know when he is alone and I want to know who around him can be bought. We will leave nothing to chance.'

Nicodemus rose to protest but Caiaphas waved him down dismissively.

'Let him into the Temple unhindered' he continued 'but never leave him alone. He is only a Galilean builder. It shouldn't be hard to pick holes in his theology. Make him look a fool in front of the people. They won't be so keen to follow him then.'

'If he does cause trouble or if he becomes too popular we will then act. If the festival is in danger or it looks like the Romans are getting too interested we will get rid of him quickly and quietly. I will not allow the festival or our nation to be put in jeopardy. After all, what is the life of one man compared to the life of the whole nation?'

He turned to his secretary. 'Make it known that this Jesus is to be watched and get me an informant from among his people. Look at the two Zealots first. They're fanatics and all fanatics are gullible. Think up a good cover story, they'll fall for it easily enough.'

He looked round at them all 'We can't afford mistakes' he said grimly. 'Just see to it!'

CHAPTER TWENTY FOUR

Jesus and the disciples left for the desert two days later but not before Nicodemus had sent word to him privately of the Council's decision. Jesus seemed remarkably calm. He had spent several hours talking at length with Lazarus and several of his friends and it appeared to Simon, as he watched from the side of the balcony, that Jesus was planning some sort of campaign. But whatever was going on, when the business was concluded Jesus gathered his disciples and took them back down the road to Jericho and out to the desert beyond.

'Wait here for me' said Jesus when they reached the caves 'I need to find the strength to face what lies ahead so I must spend time with my Father. I will be gone a few days. Don't be alarmed! I will return in time to meet up with our friends from Galilee.'

Without even waiting for a last meal with them all Jesus filled his water skin and hitched his bed roll higher on his shoulder and with ever lightening steps walked out into the desert.

The disciples watched him until he disappeared into the heat haze that shimmered over the hot broken stones. He almost appeared to be dancing and it made the disciples smile as they watched him go.

'When Jesus goes to pray he enters heaven walking on air' said Simon with a grin. 'And you know?' he looked around 'I'm beginning to feel the same. I never would have thought it but I really look forward to my prayer time.'

'Me too!' said Judas soberly. 'He's taught us well!'

***

It was already past noon on the Friday when Jesus appeared again. The disciples with Mary and Salome had packed up the camp and were standing quietly in small groups while they waited for him to appear.

John and Andrew were anxious but when Jesus appeared they could see at once that all was well. His eyes were calm and he smiled at them all. 'It is time!' he said 'Let's go!' and they walked in a companionable group towards Jericho.

The Galilean pilgrims had already begun to arrive in the little town. Its street was busy with vendors selling fruit and food for the travellers. The guest houses were full and late comers were already contemplating another night in a bed roll under the stars.

As Jesus and the disciples approached he was recognised immediately and the cry went round among the pilgrims 'He's here! Jesus is here!'

It had been several months since Jesus had disappeared from the Galilean scene and the crowds had begun to wonder if it had all been a dream. But here he was! Looking rested and fit and, followed by his team, he was with them once more.

The crowds swarmed around him as he entered the town. Hands reached out to touch him. Voices called his name and he smiled and exchanged greetings, genuinely pleased to see old friends. And there among the crowds were his mother and brothers and Peter's wife and other members of the family. Everyone was smiling and shouting. The people of the town were taken aback by the fervour of the Galileans and one, a tax collector named Zachaeus, left his booth and scrambled among the people to get a better view of what was happening. He quickly realised that he was too short to see over the mass of people and so with an agility he didn't know he possessed he shinned up the nearest large tree. From there he could look down with ease.

In the middle of the excited crowd, he could see a young man. The crowds were parting in respect as he walked, but hands were reaching out to him and the young man was responding with obvious affection. Zachaeus could see the anxious faces of his companions as they tried to surround him and protect him, but they needn't have worried. It was obvious that this young man was greatly loved.

So intent was he in watching that he was startled to the point of panic when suddenly the young man looked up and called his name. 'Zachaeus!' called Jesus with a grin 'Come down from there! I would like to stay this Sabbath night in your house. Will you invite me?'

Zachaeus was stunned 'Lord, how do you know me?' he spluttered. But Jesus just smiled and reached out a hand to help Zachaeus scramble down.

On firm ground once more Zachaeus hastily straightened his robes and looking fearfully at Jesus said 'Follow me Lord! Follow me!' and scurried across the road to a small alley way. He glanced round anxiously. Yes Jesus was indeed following him.

The by-standers from the town were also stunned. They had heard stories of this Jesus. By all accounts he was a great teacher and healer and yet of all the houses he could have visited he had chosen to stay in the house of that traitor the tax collector Zachaeus.

His friends from Galilee laughed at the townsfolk's complaints 'Wait till you get to know him' they replied with pride in their voices 'His teaching and his actions are radical but they make sense.'

'How do you mean?' demanded a burly shopkeeper.

'He says that the righteous and the important people of this world have already had their reward and therefore he must spend his time with the likes of us, the poor and the sinners. One of his favourite sayings is "The last shall be first and the first shall be last!" You should listen to him. His ideas are very refreshing.'

Zachaeus was a wealthy man. He had done well out his trade and he entertained Jesus and his disciples with great dignity and pride. When the Sabbath meal was over Jesus smiled at Zachaeus and thanked him for his hospitality and kindness.

'Will you stay the night Lord?' Zachaeus enquired tentatively.

'We would be honoured' replied Jesus 'and most grateful.'

'It is I who am grateful' whispered Zachaeus close to tears. Jesus looked at him with a smile but did not say anything. Zachaeus steadied himself. 'When I was a boy my family were poor and not very religious, but we would always celebrate the Sabbath. My mother would make the house look so beautiful and I loved the soft lights and the old words. They were comfortable.'

He gulped and continued 'But I made the decision to become a tax collector. It was the only way I could use my talent with figures to become rich. Since then no one connected with the synagogue will speak to me. As with most of the town folk they will not even return my greetings in the street. And I have stopped celebrating the Sabbath. I have my wealth but I have nothing to celebrate. Tonight is the first time for years that I have welcomed the Sabbath.'

'Each day is a new day, Zachaeus' said Jesus 'you may have put aside your faith but your Heavenly Father knows you by name and knows your every need.'

'I am such a sinner!' Zachaeus bowed his head ashamed.

'A shepherd who has lost a sheep will search all day until he finds it, and then, lifting it on to his shoulders he will return home rejoicing. So it is in heaven over one sinner that repenteth.'

Jesus stood and lifted Zachaeus to his feet. 'I am the good shepherd,' he continued. 'I know my sheep and my sheep know my voice.'

'You knew my name!' exclaimed Zachaeus his eyes wide with wonder.

'Indeed I did' said Jesus soberly looking deep into Zachaeus' eyes 'and I know what is on your heart.'

Zachaeus sunk to the ground on his knees 'Lord!' he cried 'I will give half of everything I own to the poor and if I've cheated anyone I will restore it four times over!'

Jesus laughed 'Salvation has truly come to this house' he exclaimed 'you'd better have words with Matthew. He's been down the same path. He will help you!'

The synagogues in Jericho were full to bursting the next day and the pilgrims spent the day sitting in the shade and talking to old friends. Jesus looked for his family and found them where they camped each year. He drew his mother aside. 'We may not have another chance to talk' he said placing his arms around her and holding her close. 'We are going to Jerusalem and there I will die.'

Mary's body stiffened and tears filled her eyes. 'I knew this time would come' she whispered 'The old priest Simeon warned me when I took you to the Temple as a small baby.'

'You took me then' Jesus replied sadly 'but now I go of my own free will.'

Neither of them spoke and then Jesus continued 'All the people who have come to me for healing have been so afraid. In this world even the smallest ailment untreated can lead to death. They are so desperately afraid of death and I have tried in vain to show them that God's love can conquer even death itself. Now I must die. It is the only way. I have to show them that I love them so much that I will give the thing that is most precious to us all. Life itself.'

Mary stepped back and gazed at Jesus. There was fear in her eyes and wonderment. 'Who are you, my son?' she demanded.

'You know who I am' Jesus replied with a smile. He took her hand 'you have always known and even in the darkest hour, your knowing has made my heart sing.'

'I'm glad!' she whispered and buried her head in his chest.

***

It was before dawn when the pilgrims spilled excitedly out on to the streets of Jericho ready to make the ascent to Jerusalem. The noise was considerable and the townsfolk stood in the shelter of their doorways. 'They're so excitable, these Galileans!' they said 'But never mind, they'll soon be gone and we can go back to our beds.'

Surrounded by his family and friends Jesus took the street leading out of the town. The disciples were excited. Jesus was so popular and the crowd was so big the people of Jerusalem were bound to be impressed.

They didn't hear the blind man at first. He was calling out from the side of the road and those nearest to him tried to stop him. 'Be quiet!' they cried 'Leave Jesus alone. You beggars are all the same. Nothing but scroungers!'

But Jesus suddenly stopped. He stood still and the crowd stopped with him. Then, high above the murmur of the crowd, they heard it clearly. 'Jesus, Son of David, have mercy on me!'

Jesus turned and said to Judas 'Bring him to me!' and Judas pushed his way through the crowd to where the beggar sat. 'Come on!' he said 'He's asking for you.'

The blind man jumped to his feet and clutching hold of Judas' outstretched hand he followed him eagerly in to the middle of the street.

'What do you want me to do for you Son of Timaeus?' said Jesus with a smile.

The beggar fell to the ground 'Master!' he gasped 'Let me receive my sight.'

Jesus reached out and touched the man's eyes 'Go your way' he said 'Your faith has made you well.'

Immediately the scales dropped from the beggar's eyes and he could see.

The excitement in the crowd grew. Bartimaeus was anxious not to lose sight of his saviour and followed Jesus up to the top of the escarpment and then, remembering his family, ran back to the town whooping for joy.

'He called you Son of David' said Matthew to Jesus 'That's the first time I've heard anyone call you that.'

'The blind have an uncanny knack of seeing the truth' replied Jesus.

'It is the title of the Messiah that is to come' persisted Matthew.

'It is also a title I can claim' Jesus was firm. 'Through my earthly father I am a descendant of the great King David.'

'But you never used the title before.'

'No I haven't' agreed Jesus' I have lived on this earth, among you all, as a Son of Man. I have shared your joys and your pains but today is the day for me to claim my place in history, play the part and acknowledge my ancestors.'

'And a blind man heralds this change and leads the way,' mussed Matthew 'Isaiah would approve.

"…out of their gloom and darkness
the eyes of the blind shall see.
The meek shall obtain fresh joy in the Lord,
And the poor among men shall exult in the
Holy One of Israel"'

he quoted, and then looking around at the happy and excited crowds he said 'Yes! Isaiah would certainly approve!'

CHAPTER TWENTY FIVE

It was inevitable that the crowds would tire as the journey continued. The sun was unbearably hot and the desert wind rasped at their skins but, as usual, they sang, and the singing lifted their hearts.

With Jesus among them they felt invincible. He too was a Galilean and the Galileans were a force to be reckoned with. In the past it was Galilean rebels who had stayed the course and fought invaders with distinction and no doubt they would do so in the future. And they were proud of the fact that their presence in the city at Passover time was enough to cause the governor, Pontius Pilate, to bring up three extra centuries from Caesarea just to keep control.

So it was, with aching feet but with spirits high, they reached the Mount of Olives late in the afternoon and at Jesus' instigation they stopped at the cross roads between the twin villages of Bethany and Bethpage.

Jesus called Andrew and John to him and said 'Go over into the village and you will find an ass tethered outside a house. Untie it and bring it here.'

'Just take it, you mean?' asked John.

'If someone questions you tell them that I have need of it. We will return it later.'

John and Andrew ran off and Jesus sat for a while on the grass. It wasn't possible to actually see the city from this point but, only a few yards further along, the road reached its highest point and they knew the city would then lie at their feet. Every year the first sight of the city would send the pilgrims into frenzy. It was the highlight of their journey and they were happy, for the moment, to delay its happening.

Matthew sat on the grass next to Jesus 'Why an ass?' he enquired.

Jesus looked at him quizzically. 'How did the first son of David ride into Jerusalem?'

Matthew thought for a while. 'Why, it was Solomon, and Zadok and Nathan anointed him at Gihon while his brother Adonijah was already celebrating because he thought that he would be made king. Then,' continued Matthew, 'Solomon rode on the king's ass and, with the ordinary people lining the street, he rode to the palace and claimed the throne and the kingdom.'

'You see' said Jesus with a smile 'you were right when you quoted from Isaiah, for I too will be accompanied by the ordinary people of this land. The meek shall indeed find fresh joy in the Lord and the poor among men shall exult in the Holy One of Israel.'

'Are you going to claim the Kingdom after all?'

'I am going to claim a crown and a Kingdom, but my Kingship and my Kingdom are not of this world.' Jesus sounded weary, but as John and Andrew arrived with the young ass between them he got to his feet and saying quietly to himself 'Behold Jerusalem, your King is coming!' and he climbed on the back of the animal.

Seeing Jesus seated on the ass a cry went up among the pilgrims and scrambling to their feet they rushed to gather around.

Andrew led the ass and the disciples quickly closed ranks as it walked sedately along the road picking its feet carefully to avoid the stones. Jesus sat tall on its back and although he smiled at those who clamoured round him his eyes were still and sad.

Mary could hardly bear to watch and Matthew moved to her side 'It's all part of his plan,' he said with a grimace 'and it would seem that it's all part of God's plan too. Though where it will lead him I really can't guess!'

'I can!' said Mary sadly and she looked at the excited crowds 'Why can't they see what's happening? How can they be so happy?'

The crowd was erupting with joy and expectation. Men took off their cloaks to lay then down on the road so that the little ass didn't stumble on the rocky path and others pulled down branches from the trees and waved them excitedly.

'Hosanna to the Son of David' they cried 'Blessed is he who comes in the name of the Lord.'

Among the pilgrims from Galilee were the Pharisees and one of them ran to come alongside Jesus. 'Rabbi' he said 'tell your disciples to be quiet. What they are saying is dangerous. It could get you into serious trouble.'

Jesus smiled 'I tell you this. If these were silent, the very stones would cry out!'

They reached the summit of the mount and before descending to the Kidron Valley many in the crowd began to sing the Hallel psalms while others continued to shout and wave their branches. In the midst of all the turmoil Jesus sat, a still quiet figure. He would not make this Passover journey again and tears filled his eyes as he looked at the city ahead. 'Such a proud and beautiful city!' he said 'But the day is coming when enemies will smash you to the ground, you and all your people, because you were blind and did not recognise who it is who has come to save you!'

And so they descended to the valley floor and made their way up to the Golden Gate of the Temple straight into the open court of the Gentiles. The court was busy with pilgrims and traders and resembled a large market place. Andrew took the ass and tethered it at the gate while the still excited crowd of Galileans pushed their way into the open space inside.

As usual it was their custom to pay the half shekel Temple tax before making for the campsite. First, though, their denari must be changed to staters because the tax could only be paid in this ancient Tyrian coin which was the closest thing to the old shekel.

The Galilean pilgrims went straight to the money changers' tables. There was some good natured jostling to get to the front of the queue but then, suddenly, an eruption of noise around one of the tables, followed by a slam of a fist on the table and a loud roar, caused everyone to look up suddenly. John and James were in the midst of the tumult, their faces red with rage.

Jesus caught their eye. 'We can't afford this rate of exchange!' shouted John across the heads of the other pilgrims.

'They're demanding too much!' James was so angry he could barely speak.

'I don't have that sort of money' added Andrew 'I won't be able to pay my Temple tax after all!'

'They're crooks!' shouted John again in his disappointment and anger and the crowd pushed in behind him with fists raised and voices shrill with indignation. 'You should be ashamed!' 'Cheats!' 'I've saved all year to pay this tax!' 'How are we supposed to find this money?' 'Thieves!'

Matthew caught Jesus' arm 'Look!' he said urgently 'Up there, by the tower!'

Alerted by the noise soldiers were spilling out of their barracks on to the top of the colonnades.

Jesus moved immediately. He strode forward and the pilgrims stopped their noise and moved back to let him through. The soldiers watched and made no further movement. When he reached the tables Jesus asked 'So what is the rate of exchange?'

Confident of their position as licensed money changers who had the approval of the High Priest, one of the money changers snapped imperiously 'Two denarii for one half shekel.'

Jesus looked shocked 'That's equal to two day's wages' he said grimly 'on top of the tax itself that's beyond the reach of most men here!'

'Take it or leave it!' the man shrugged.

'No!' said Jesus angrily 'The people have come in good faith to pay their taxes so that this Temple can be maintained to the glory of God, as a place of prayer. But you, with your greed, have turned it into a market place. You have made my Father's house a den of thieves!'

He looked around in disgust at the traders and their stalls and the traffic of people making a short cut through the court from the city beyond out through to the Golden Gate.

'It's you who must go!' he said with anger in his voice and he reached down catching the corner of the table in front and tipped its contents on to the floor.

The pilgrims looked on in amazement and then following his lead they rushed forward to tip the other tables, leaving the stall holders scrabbling on the floor searching for the rolling coins.

Not content with just disrupting the exchange the pilgrims moved as a mass towards the animal stalls, and the traders left their places and fled as pens were opened and animals were freed to roam.

'Stop the people using this court as a thoroughfare!' ordered Jesus and as men ran to do his bidding quiet gradually descended on the court. From the colonnade the Roman soldiers watched with interest. From the steps leading to the Court of the Women three white robed priests stood with their mouths expressing shock and horror. All around Jesus in the Court of the Gentiles people stopped and looked at him. What was going to happen now?

In the silence that followed a lamb bleated. Then Jesus lifted up his arms. 'Who shall ascend the hill of the Lord' he called 'Who shall stand in his holy place?' and the pilgrims responded with tears in their eyes 'He who has clean hands and a pure heart, who does not lift up his soul to what is false.'

And Jesus continued and his voice was loud in exultation. 'Lift up your heads, O Gates! And be lifted up, O ancient doors!'

'That the King of Glory may come in!' the crowd replied.

'Who is this King of Glory?' demanded Jesus.

'The Lord of Hosts! He is the King of Glory!' they shouted in triumph looking defiantly at the gathering number of priests on the steps.

And then, striding through the crowds, Jesus walked to the Golden Gate and the pilgrims followed him. They stepped through into the darkening shadows of the Kidron Valley leaving behind them a deserted courtyard.

From high on the top of the colonnade a Roman soldier laughed.

CHAPTER TWENTY SIX

They were to spend that night as guests of Lazarus and his sisters and so, while the other pilgrims from Galilee made their camps on the Mount of Olives Jesus led his party up the stony path to the village of Bethany.

Lazarus was standing by his gate anxious for their arrival and his servants took their dusty sandals and robes and washed their feet and found them clean fresh clothing. Without more ado, Jesus and his companions were lead through into a room where a low table was groaning under the weight of beautifully prepared food. 'Don't stand on ceremony' said Lazarus with a smile 'Eat!'

The disciples didn't hesitate and although Judas looked a little uncomfortable in the lavish surroundings he eagerly sank on to the cushions and reached out for food. The wine flowed freely and after such a long walk everyone relaxed into a sleepy contentment.

'What I liked about you, Jesus' said Judas rather pointedly, 'was that you seemed to care about the poor people of this world.'

Jesus raised an eyebrow and turned to meet his gaze.

'And it was the poor people who accompanied you into Jerusalem and the poor you defended just now in the Temple' Judas went on and then he stopped not certain how to continue.

At that moment Lazarus' younger sister Mary came into the room. She was carrying a delicate bottle and she came to Jesus and knelt beside him. Removing the stopper she poured ointment over his feet and wiped them with her hair. The house was filled with fragrance and Judas spoke up roughly. 'That's what I'm trying to say' he blurted out angrily. 'Surely that is spikenard, the most expensive perfume on earth. Instead of wasting it like that it could have been sold and the money given to the poor. Why that amount is worth three hundred denarii at least!'

He sat back flushing as if suddenly aware of his rudeness to his hosts.

Jesus smiled at him and said 'Let her alone Judas. She can keep the rest of it for the day of my burial. The poor you will always have with you, but you will not always have me.'

Judas was silent and a few minutes later he left the table and made for the door. Outside in the night air he stood at the side of the house and looked up at the night sky. The smell of summer jasmine filled the air and he took a deep breath.

He hadn't intended such an outburst. He admired Jesus more than anyone he had ever met. He would not hurt him for the world. It's just that Jesus seemed to have some rich friends and Judas found it puzzling how Jesus could justify their place in the ranks of his followers. Surely his teaching about the meek and the poor inheriting the earth meant that the rich were beyond the pale. Surely that's how it should be!

A light tap on his shoulder caused him to jump round in surprise. A Pharisee with grey hair and beard stood beside him. 'It's Judas isn't it?' he asked.

'Yes!' he said warily 'How do you know my name?'

'You were pointed out to me' said the Pharisee with a winning smile 'I was told you were a man with a marked social conscience and a true and faithful follower of this man Jesus.'

Judas nodded 'So?' he enquired.

'I believe your Jesus is a good man' said the Pharisee 'I respect his teaching. He could really make a name for himself in this city. You could help1'

'How?' asked Judas eagerly.

'I have a friend who is secretary to the High Priest himself. He could put a word in for your Jesus. No-one can get anywhere in Jerusalem without Caiaphas' backing.'

Judas' eyes gleamed with excitement 'Do you think he would put a word in?' he exclaimed 'Why if Jesus had the High Priest's backing then no-one would dare oppose him!'

'Exactly so!' agreed the Pharisee 'Would you like to meet my friend and see what he can do?'

'Definitely' said Judas 'This might just be the answer to all our problems.'

'He lives here in this village' said the Pharisee. 'His name is Malchus. Shall we go and see if he's in?'

'Yes let's go now' said Judas in a voice tinged with excitement 'There's no time to waste!'

Malchus' house was in darkness when they approached and Judas' heart sank in disappointment but after a hurried whisper to a servant who appeared with a lamp, the side gate was opened and the two men were allowed in.

Malchus was a fleshy, rather pompous looking man but although he was already in his night attire he very quickly made Judas feel at ease. The best wine was brought and warm slippers were eased on to his feet.

'I have heard such good things about your master' his voice was smooth and his eyes watched Judas' every reaction. 'I'm sure I can arrange for the High Priest to meet him.'

Judas was excited.

'Of course my master is a busy man, and so I expect is yours' mused Malchus. 'With the feast approaching I'm not sure how we can arrange it. Caiaphas has so many meetings to attend.'

Disappointed again Judas didn't reply.

'Perhaps Caiaphas would agree to an evening meeting in the privacy of his own house' said Malchus looking at Judas enquiringly 'would your master be free of an evening? With all the crowds out of the way he and Caiaphas could have a quiet talk.'

'Yes!' agree Judas eagerly. 'I'm sure that would be best.'

'I expect your master has plans' said Malchus watching Judas carefully 'do you know if he has a free moment one evening before the feast?'

'No I don't' Judas was crest-fallen.

'Never mind!' said Malchus airily 'When you see an opportunity arising send me word and I will come to where he is and invite him in person and escort him to Caiaphas!'

Judas was stunned 'Why would you put yourself out like that?' he said.

'My dear young man' replied Malchus 'your master is a very important man. Look at the things he has done. The whole world should know about him. Caiaphas would be furious with me if I didn't offer him the utmost of courtesies.' Then he smiled at Judas 'And I wouldn't be surprised if he didn't reward you handsomely for making it all possible.'

Judas looked shocked 'Reward me! Oh no! That's not what I'm here for!'

Malchus smiled again. 'Nevertheless I'm sure there will be a gift of some sort for your services. If you don't want it you can always give it to the poor.'

Judas' eyes flickered and Malchus smiled again 'Shall we say thirty pieces of silver?' he said.

CHAPTER TWENTY SEVEN

The following morning the women stayed in Bethany while Jesus led his disciples down to the Temple. They grouped around Jesus as they walked in through the Gate and flanked him closely as they walked briskly across the Court of Gentiles and climbed the steps into the Court of Women. Here the atmosphere was quieter with groups of men under the porticoes listening to the teachers. All the alcoves were taken and so Jesus led them to the space in front of the treasury boxes and here he perched on the edge of a small limestone wall. Other pilgrims seeing him arrive moved across to join him. For a moment he sat watching as people put their donations into the box. Many people came and threw in large sums and then an elderly woman wearing black came forward and, digging deep in her purse found two copper coins which she quietly dropped in the box before going on her way.

Jesus turned to his disciples and the gathering crowd. 'That little widow has given the most expensive gift of all' he said, causing them to look puzzled. 'All the others have plenty and their gifts didn't hurt them at all, but she had nothing except those two coins, so she gave everything she had, her whole living!'

As he spoke a group of priests and elders approached and looking at the crowd beginning to gather they turned to Jesus angrily. 'Who gave you permission to hold a gathering here? What authority do you have?'

The disciples looked alarmed but Jesus remained calm. 'I will answer your question if you will first answer mine' he said.

They were all taken aback. They hadn't expected a builder from Galilee to have so much confidence. They didn't answer him but looked at him open mouthed.

'Tell me!' ordered Jesus 'Did John the Baptist obtain a certificate from the religious authorities giving him permission to preach or did his authority come from God alone?'

In panic the elders huddled together. 'If we say he received his authority from men the crowd will lynch us because they all believe John was a prophet. If we say "from God" he will claim the same authority and we will have no authority to stop him. He's cleverer than we were led to believe!'

On of them stepped forward 'We can't answer you' he mumbled.

Jesus looked at them sternly 'Then neither will I answer your question' he said dismissively and got to his feet.

A group of Pharisees came and stood by the Temple officials. They looked imposing and such a show of strength was meant to be intimidating. Judas hurried to Jesus' side 'Master!' he whispered urgently 'I met someone last night who could get you permission to preach.'

'Did you Judas?' replied Jesus looking directly into Judas' eyes. 'So you have taken the first step. My time will not be long now.'

Judas felt a thrill of pride. He should have known that Jesus would guess at what he planned. With Caiaphas' personal authority Jesus would at last be in a position to bring about his Kingdom.

'The Chief Priest wants to meet with you' Judas spoke quietly. 'He said one evening this week would suit him well. When shall I tell him you will be free?'

'After our Passover meal. I have much to do before then' Jesus replied. 'But say nothing to the others. Let it be our secret!'

Judas was thrilled. He'd always known he would be a key player in Jesus' plan. Now he knew that with his help and his contacts Jesus couldn't help but succeed. He stood back his eyes gleaming with excitement. Soon, very soon the kingdom would come!

Another group of men, dressed more sumptuously, joined the Pharisees. 'Herodians!' Andrew nudged John 'What do they want?'

One of the Pharisees stepped forward 'Master!' he said addressing Jesus with great reverence. 'We know you to be an honest and faithful teacher of God's word. We know too that you cannot be bought and are not influenced by the politics of man.'

Jesus' eyes narrowed.

'Tell us then,' the Pharisee continued 'should we Jews pay taxes to Caesar, or not?'

There was a sudden silence. This was a trick question equal to the one he, Jesus, had asked. Either way he could be in trouble. If he said yes the Jews should pay he would make himself very unpopular with the crowd. If he said no he could be instantly arrested for insurrection.

The crowd held its breath.

Jesus looked the questioner in the eye. 'Show me the coins you use for paying the tax!' he ordered.

The Pharisee looked confused and one of the Herodians impatiently tugged at his money bag hanging from his belt. 'Here!' he said handing the Pharisee a denarius.

The Pharisee took the coin disdainfully and held it up to Jesus.

'Look at it!' said Jesus 'Whose head and inscription is on the coin?'

'Caesar's!' said the Pharisee without bothering to look.

'If it is Caesar's coin then we should give it back to him' replied Jesus making the crowd smile 'But!' he added firmly 'If we pay Caesar what he is due, as good Jews we must first and foremost make sure that we pay God what he is due. Caesar minted this coin and we pay him back in coin. God gives us his love and we must pay him back with love.'

The Pharisees stood in a confused silence while the crowd grinned happily to see them bested. Then one of them stood forward. 'Rabbi!' he asked 'Which of the commandments do you think is the greatest?'

Without hesitation Jesus replied 'You shall love the Lord your god with all your heart and with all your soul, and with all your mind. This is the first and greatest commandment. And a second is like it, you shall love your neighbour as yourself.'

He looked at the Pharisee who had asked the question 'Wouldn't you agree that on these two commandments depend all the law and the prophets?'

The man nodded 'Yes master I would!' he answered 'You have answered well!' Then, as his companions turned to scowl at him, he turned and walked thoughtfully away.

The leader of the religious group pulled the others aside 'We're supposed to be making him look a fool and instead he's running rings round us! Caiaphas will be furious!'

'It's early days yet!' said his companion. 'If we stay with him he's bound to make a mistake sooner or later.'

One of the Herodians nudged him. 'Here come the Sadducees. Let's see if they can do any better!'

Dressed in the height of fashion a group of Sadducees bustled forward. Everybody looked at them expectantly. What question were they going to ask?

Taken aback by the silence of the crowd and Jesus' calm demeanour as he waited for them to speak, their spokesman blustered. 'We hear you follow the Pharisees teaching' he said 'that you believe in a resurrection and a life after this one.'

Jesus did not reply and the man became aggressive 'Well!' he said 'Answer me this if you can! Moses says that if a man dies, having no children, his brother must marry the widow.' The disciples began to laugh and the man, not knowing what had caused the laughter, flushed and struggled to continue 'And he must raise up children for his brother.' He paused and took a deep breath 'Now there were seven brothers and' he got no further for the disciples were beside themselves with mirth.

The man was puzzled and Jesus turned to his companions and said sternly 'Let him speak now!'

The man began again and struggled to the end of his story and then triumphantly turned to Jesus 'In the resurrection, then, to which of the seven will she be wife? For they all had her!'

Laughter erupted again and Jesus too smiled 'You Sadducees are so wrong in your ideas' he said 'in the resurrection there will be no human ties of marriage but in the presence of God, who is love, we will all be bound together by love, and as for the resurrection itself have you not read in the scriptures that God said of Himself "I am the God of Abraham, of Isaac and of Jacob?" He says "I am" not "I was" for Abraham, Isaac and Jacob still live!'

The Pharisees nodded knowingly and the Sadducees looked confused. They were not serious scholars, only adhering to the party line. They didn't know if Jesus' argument held up or not. They stood in sulky silence.

Then Jesus irritated by the sullen opposition seemed to make up his mind to take the initiative. He stood straight and preached to them directly. 'Hear this parable!' he said 'There was a house holder who planted a vineyard, put a hedge round it, dug a wine press and built a tower. All the hard work was done for it to be a successful vineyard but then he needed to go away so he let it out to tenants.'

'After the first harvest he sent his servants to collect the rent and his portion of the harvest but the tenants beat one of the servants, stoned another and killed the third. So he sent more servants and the tenants did the same. Finally he sent his son thinking that the tenants will surely respect his son, but the tenants thought that if they killed the son they could claim his inheritance, so they took him and killed him.'

Then Jesus asked 'and what do you think the owner of the vineyard will do when he returns home?'

The elders looked at him stunned and a young boy in the front of the group of pilgrims said eagerly 'He will put those wretches to a miserable death!'

'You are right,' agreed Jesus and looking up at the elders again he said severely 'therefore, I tell you, the Kingdom of God will be taken away from you and given to those who produce the fruit of love and pay God with the harvest of this love.'

The elders blanched and the crowd gasped. Judas began to panic. What was Jesus doing? Didn't he realise that he needed these people as friends? It was obvious that he was equating the religious leaders with the tenants. Why was he deliberately antagonising them?

The elders did not move. They stood solidly together and then in exasperation the Sadducees and Herodians moved away, their backs rigid with disapproval. The Pharisees and scribes remained, not knowing what to say but determined to watch for any little weakness Jesus might show. Another large group of black robed Pharisees joined them and they hovered around the edges of the pilgrims like vultures waiting for the kill.

But Jesus was showing no signs of weakness and to the crowd's delight, and Judas' secret horror, he began to denounce them roundly. 'You scribes and Pharisees' he declared 'you have been entrusted by God to care for his people, to instruct them in the law and to lead them into God's Kingdom. But' he said raising his voice angrily 'you do not practice what you preach!'

He turned to the crowds 'Do as they say but don't ever try to live as they do, for they are hypocrites! They think that their fancy prayer shawls and ornate phylacteries make them holy. They love being given the place of honour at feasts and they adore the respect you show them in the streets. But they make no effort to help you reach the Kingdom. Instead they load burdens on to your backs in the way of rules and regulations and when you stumble and fall they make no effort to help you.'

'They are blind guides for they only pretend to know the way to the Kingdom of God but they are more concerned about petty things like tithing and washing and these petty observances slam the door to the Kingdom in the faces of those who are trying to seek the way!'

Looking directly at the furious group of Pharisees Jesus lifted his hand and pointed at them angrily 'Woe to you, scribes and Pharisees, hypocrites! For you are like white washed tombs, which outwardly appear beautiful, but within they are full of dead men's bones and all uncleanness. So you also outwardly appear righteous to men, but within you are full of hypocrisy and iniquity.'

The crowd gasped. Never before had anyone dared to speak like this. The Pharisees were too taken aback to speak. Their faces white with anger and indignation they were rooted to the spot.

But Jesus hadn't finished with them. 'You serpents!' he spoke fiercely 'You brood of vipers! How are you going to escape being sentenced to hell?'

'How dare you!' spluttered one of the young Pharisees pushing his way to the front.

'I do dare!' replied Jesus sternly. 'You are the religious leaders of this land and God has entrusted the care of his people to you and yet when he sends prophets and wise men to help you what do you do? You kill then, scourge them and stone them! Because of you this generation will be punished. Because of you God's vineyard will be occupied by strangers.'

He paused and then with his eyes intense and burning black with fire he spoke again. His voice echoed around the court and people stopped in their tracks to listen. 'O Jerusalem!' he cried from the heart 'You kill the prophets and stone those who are sent to help you. Yet I long to gather your children together and protect them as a hen gathers her brood under he wings. But you don't want this. You turn your back on such love and so the city will be laid bare. It will become desolate and forsaken!'

Then he stopped speaking and stood still in front of them all.

Nobody moved. They had never witnessed such a drama before. No one spoke, and then Jesus sat down heavily on the wall behind him and Simon hurried forward to sit beside him. 'That's enough for one day!' he said anxiously 'There's still a long way to go. Conserve your strength!'

'You're right Simon!' said Jesus with a wry smile. 'We should go now, before I say something contentious!'

Simon laughed and, putting his hand under Jesus' elbow, looked up at the expectant faces of the crowd 'The Master has finished for the day' he said firmly 'you can go on your way!'

One of the Pharisees barked out a laugh 'Finished!' he declared 'I'll say he is!' and with that the Pharisees turned away as one man, their black cloaks swirling behind them as they stalked angrily across the courtyard.

Judas was non-plussed. What on earth had made Jesus speak so rashly? How could he possibly expect the High Priest's help now? He hurried to follow Jesus out of the Temple, his mind racing. Was there a way he could retrieve the situation? Dare he arrange another meeting? Could the harm be undone? Judas was bemused. Surely Jesus' whole mission depended on having Caiaphas' support.

CHAPTER TWENTY EIGHT

As they left the Temple building to walk through the Golden Gate and out to the Kidron Valley, Thomas ran to walk beside Jesus. 'Have you looked at the stone work in detail?' he asked 'Look how every block is edged to make an exact fit.' His professional interest was aroused 'It's taken over forty years to build and the workman still haven't finished. Why some of those stones are so heavy and fit so exactly the Temple will probably stand for thousands of years!'

Jesus looked sad 'No Thomas!' he said 'This building, however grand and well built, will fall. Not one stone will be left upon another; they will all be thrown down.'

The disciples exchanged worried glances but it wasn't until they paused in their walk on the slopes of the Mount of Olives and sat on the boulders overlooking the Temple that they plucked up courage to ask questions.

'When will this happen?' demanded Thomas anxiously, looking down on to the gleaming white limestone walls, porticoes and turrets of the beautiful building below them.

'Sooner than you think' replied Jesus solemnly 'this present generation will live to see it all and the destruction will be terrible. There will be more distress than there has ever been before, even since the beginning of the world.'

The disciples looked alarmed and Jesus continued 'And this poor city with all its people will bear the brunt of the suffering. When the armies come to destroy these buildings they will kill all who oppose them. The townsfolk must not hope to be spared. They should flee, even the elderly and the very young, and the mothers with babies. They should flee as far away as possible. Let us hope for their sakes that it is not winter when this disaster strikes.'

'But how will people know? What can they do to protect themselves?' asked Mary her eyes wide with fear.

'They must be alert' replied Jesus 'just as the new leaves on this fig tree herald the coming of summer so people must learn to read the signs of this world.' He got to his feet and looked down on them all 'They must make it their business to stay awake to what is happening around them. They can't afford to be complacent. They need to know the political moves that are being made, then they can take precautions and care for themselves and their families. The time will definitely come, and soon!'

'What should we do?' demanded Simon.

'Why Simon,' Jesus replied with a smile 'you won't be here! You will be out fishing, fishing for men!'

A puzzled frown appeared on Simon's face and Jesus continued 'It won't be easy for any of you either. You must be on your guard! You will go into the world to spread the news of God's love. Everyone must hear the message!'

'Leave Israel you mean?' asked John.

'Yes!' replied Jesus firmly 'Before the end the gospel must be proclaimed to all nations!'

'But are we ready to go out into the world?' Andrew looked frightened.

Jesus was more gentle. 'Remember when I sent you out before Andrew?' Andrew nodded dumbly. 'Were you ready then?'

'Not really!' muttered Andrew.

'But once you started you were not afraid. You knew what to do and what to say. Why was that?'

It was John who replied 'Because we all felt that somehow you were with us and that gave us courage!'

The others nodded.

'I'm not going to lie to you' Jesus continued 'people will hate you for your allegiance to me. You will be beaten and stoned. You will be arrested and you will have to testify in courts, but, just as before, I will be with you. My spirit will give you courage and I will give you the words to say.'

He looked down at the Temple and the busy streets of the city and his voice lifted. 'All of this will pass away' he said 'heaven and earth will pass away, but my words will live for ever!'

The disciples' faces were glum and uncomprehending. The way ahead looked grim. Not at all what they had expected. Jesus smiled at them all. 'Come on now!' he urged 'Let us return to Bethany. Martha was already cooking when we left this morning. She should have finished by now.'

The disciples scrambled obediently to their feet.

'Come and walk with me Judas' said Jesus looking into the confused eyes of his most fervent disciple 'We have many things to talk about!' A look of relief passed over Judas' face. At last Jesus and he could make plans. All may not be lost.

Waiting until the others had gone on ahead of them Judas was impatient to question Jesus. 'Why did you jeopardise our plan and antagonise the Pharisees?' he demanded.

'Our plan Judas?' Jesus' voice was calm.

'Yes! Yes!' Judas could barely keep his excitement contained 'I've arranged for you to meet the High Priest himself on Thursday evening, and you agreed!'

Jesus didn't speak for a while and then nodded his head 'Yes Judas, I will meet with the High Priest that night.'

Judas breathed a sigh of relief 'He is going to help you! He admires your teaching. He will back you!'

Jesus sighed 'Judas you are truly a zealot. You are full of enthusiasm and see only what you want to see. This makes you very vulnerable!'

Judas was aggrieved 'But it's the truth. Malchus his secretary told me so.'

'Be wary Judas!' said Jesus 'Be on your guard. I send you disciples out like sheep among wolves; I don't want any of you to lose your innocence and your trust but it would be sensible to be as wary as serpents. People are not always what they seem.'

Uncertain what to say Judas walked on in silence. It was obvious Jesus thought him naive, and this opinion did nothing to give him comfort. It was obvious too that he had to show Jesus that he could carry out this plan in a mature and sensible manner. Then Jesus would have to acknowledge his assistance. He would have to acknowledge that because of him, Judas, his Kingdom could become a reality.

By the time they reached Bethany Judas had run over his plan in his mind and was almost euphoric. Jesus needed his help and he would deliver; he couldn't fail! Later that evening, leaving the others, he slipped round to Malchus' house. He was excited and not a little nervous. What if the High Priest had changed his mind after hearing of Jesus' outburst in the Temple.

He needn't have worried. Malchus was all smiles and welcoming. Yes the High Priest had heard of the trouble Jesus had had with the Pharisees. They were so po-faced agreed Malchus that it was difficult not to get upset by them. No, the High Priest didn't blame Jesus at all. If anything it showed that Jesus was a man of truth who spoke as he found. Caiaphas was looking forward to the meeting.

Judas let out a sigh of relief. 'We are having a meal together on Thursday evening somewhere in the city. I don't know where exactly' he said 'but afterwards we are going out to the Garden of Gethsemane and will camp there under the olive trees. I thought that once the others were settled I could bring Jesus to you.' He looked eagerly at Malchus 'Where should I bring him?'

'My dear young man' exclaimed Malchus 'I wouldn't dream of allowing you or your master to walk alone through the streets at night. Just let me know when the meal is finished and I will bring a body guard and come and fetch your master in person. I will be at Caiaphas' house. Find me there' he smiled encouragingly 'it would afford me the greatest of pleasures to be allowed to escort Jesus. I too have longed to meet him. What an amazing young man he is!'

Judas' chest puffed out with pride. 'We think he is the Messiah' he confided.

'Yes!' said Malchus fingering his chin. 'I've heard people say that too!' He patted Judas' arm. 'If that's the case then we definitely need Caiaphas' support. He will know exactly what to do!'

CHAPTER TWENTY NINE

When he visited Jerusalem over the next few days Jesus was careful to remain surrounded by his disciples and to stay with the crowds. He found a place in the Temple porticoes to sit quietly and speak to all who came. At night he often returned to Bethany but on occasions he would join the other Galilean pilgrims in the gardens. They went to the Temple to offer their sacrifices and took away their meat for the Passover and he spent a lot of time in the streets with the ordinary people. Ever popular with the crowds from Galilee, his popularity slowly grew among the people of the city. He was a dignified, articulate young man and it was difficult to find fault in him even though the black robed scribes obviously disapproved.

On the Thursday morning as they walked down the Mount, Jesus called Simon, James and John to him and said 'I want you to prepare our Passover meal for tonight.'

'A day early?' enquired James.

I need to have one last meal with you all together' insisted Jesus 'and it needs to be tonight. I have brought the lamb' and he handed over the portion of meat to James who took it with a puzzled frown.

'Where will we have the meal?' asked James.

'I am not telling you now' Jesus replied quietly 'I don't want the meal interrupted unexpectantly.'

'I know you're nervous of the authorities' said James 'but you don't have to keep secrets from us. None of us will betray you!'

'Nevertheless' said Jesus 'I would rather the place was kept a secret until tonight.'

James couldn't help allowing his puzzlement to show and Jesus continued, speaking quietly so that the three men had to draw close.

'Go to the pool of Siloam. There will be a man standing there and he will be carrying a pitcher of water. When he sees you he will begin to walk away. Follow him' said Jesus 'and he will lead you to an upper room. When you get there spend the day getting ready for a meal tonight!'

'A man with a pitcher of water!' exclaimed John with a laugh 'He'll stand out in the crowd alright.'

'That's the idea John!' said Jesus. 'Follow him but don't go too close and don't speak to him. Make it look casual. I want to avoid the authorities today and they've got spies everywhere!'

It was as Jesus had said. Leaning against the white washed wall near the pool there was indeed a man with a pitcher of water on his shoulder. Only it was a younger man than they expected; a teenager with a slightly built frame, curly black hair and coal black eyes.

Waiting for a moment after he was certain the disciples had seen him the boy began casually to walk away back in to the city. A moment or so later the disciples followed, chatting among themselves and showing no signs that they were doing anything other than walking in towards the shops. The teenager led them through a maze of little streets climbing upwards towards the newer more gracious buildings that had only recently been built on the higher areas inside the wall. Then the young lad slipped in through a door of one of the houses whose wall ran immediately adjacent to the street. As he disappeared he indicated with a quick point of a finger towards a flight of steps alongside the house.

The disciples did not follow immediately but walked along up the street until they reached the busy thoroughfare leading to Herod's palace with its three tall towers. Here they bought a few things from the busy street traders and then after checking that they were not being followed they doubled back down the road to the house and, climbing the stone stairs, opened the door which led into an upper chamber. There were rugs on the floor and a low table and cushions. On a side cupboard were plates and mugs. A door on to a roof top veranda led out to a brazier with a stock of wood and charcoal. They had everything they needed.

'At last' said John to Simon 'now we're going to find out if you really can cook!'

Simon groaned 'I've told you. I can only cook fish!'

'It can't be that hard!' said James undoing the cloth that held the piece of lamb and folding back the palm leaves that kept the juices from leaking.

'You better do it then!' said Simon thankfully. 'We'll deal with everything else.'

'I'll need herbs and spices and, although we bought the bread just now, we'll need plenty of wine.' James was already looking for a knife and seemed eager to get on. He looked up at Simon, 'Did Judas give you enough money?'

Simon put his hand in his money bag and his waist and pulled out a few silver coins. 'Plenty!' he said 'Judas was upset not to be coming with us!' added John 'He was quite ready to have a sulk until Jesus had a quiet word.'

'He was quite edgy' agreed Simon 'Still this city is enough to make anyone tense. I'll be glad to get back to the lake.'

'Go and get the herbs and the wine first. There's a good chap!' said James with a laugh. 'And make sure Caiaphas' spies don't see you!'

When they returned they found the brazier lit and the meat braising. The smell was delicious and John was full of admiration. 'I had no idea you could be so domesticated' he said to his brother.

James gave a laugh of embarrassment.'I had some help' he admitted 'when you left the young lad came up to see what was going on.'

A light step caused them to turn to the stairs 'Here he is again!' exclaimed James 'Mark come here and meet my brother John and my friend Simon.'

The teenager stepped forward eagerly. 'Are you disciples of Jesus too?' he asked taking the hand of Simon proffered him.

'Indeed we are' exclaimed Simon 'Do you know Jesus?' he asked.

'No! But I was in the Temple when he had a go at those Pharisees. What a man! Would he have me as a disciple do you think?'

John laughed 'I'm sure he'd love that' he said 'but I have a feeling that it's too late!' He became suddenly serious 'Something is going to happen soon. I don't know what it is but Jesus seems to be preparing for the end.'

Not to be deterred Mark persisted 'Is he coming here tonight?' he asked and when Simon nodded he continued 'Will it be alright if I come up here and see him?'

The three men looked at each other and then Simon said 'Come up and tend the fire and be here when he arrives but when we sit down for the meal you'd better disappear. I know Jesus wants this meal to be a private time with us all.'

Mark's eyes gleamed. He looked at James 'If Mother protests you'll tell her it's alright, won't you?'

James smiled 'I'll tell her' he agreed.

Simon and John looked puzzled. James gave a rueful shrug 'Well alright!' he said reluctantly. 'His mother came up too when you were out. Mark lit the fire and Mary, that's his mother, chopped and seasoned the meat. All I've had to do is to turn it over and let it cook gently!' John laughed and James continued 'She's coming back to finish off in a minute' he said 'She's some relation to Nicodemus I think.'

'My father was Nicodemus' ward' explained Mark. 'He died three years ago. Mother and I live here alone.'

He looked around at the room 'the house is really too big for us now' he said sadly 'but if we can let this room out occasionally we get a little money. Passover is a good time for us!'

It was well after dark when Jesus and the other disciples slipped in through the city gates and hurriedly made their way through the darkened streets to Mary's house.

Climbing the steps they reached the roof terraced where Mark was standing by the brazier. His young face gleamed in the fire light and his black eyes sparkled with excitement. Jesus walked over to him and for a few short moments they talked quietly while the disciples stood back to give them space. Then Jesus touched the boys' arm and Mark lifted a hand and turning on his heels ran back down the stairs.

Opening the door to the Upper Room the disciples filed in following Jesus. Peter, James and John had worked hard and the room looked comfortable and inviting. Lamps were set on small niches around the room and their light gave a soft glow that picked out the deep red woven wool of the cushions and rugs. The table was laden with food and pitchers containing wine and other full of water stood ready at the corners.

The disciples hesitated in the doorway and Jesus beckoned them in. 'Come in!' he said 'Take off your shoes and sit down. We are alone tonight and we must manage for ourselves.'

Kicking their shoes off by the door the young men stepped gingerly over the cushions and sat down. Taking a jug of water Jesus poured some into a bowl and putting a towel over his arm came and knelt down by the side of Nathaniel.

'Let me wash your feet' he said and before Nathaniel could protest he poured water from the bowl and began to clean the dust and grime from Nathaniel's feet.

The disciples fell silent and Jesus deftly patted the feet clean and moved on to Simon. Simon drew his feet back in horror 'That's a servant's job Jesus!' he said 'I can't let you wait on me like this.'

Jesus laughed 'All men are precious in God's sight Simon. The master and the slave are equal.' He took a firm hold of one of Simon's big feet 'I am here among you today as a servant, just as each of you will go out into the world as God's servants.' He looked up at Simon 'If you can't allow me to show my love for you in this way then we cannot truly be one.'

Simon flushed and thrust his feet forward quickly. 'Wash my feet!' he begged 'And wash my whole body too!'

Everyone laughed 'It's only your feet that need washing Simon' replied Jesus 'Don't push it!'

When Jesus had joined them at the table they all solemnly stood and John asked the question. 'Why is this night different from all other nights?' and Jesus, as the host, replied with the old familiar words and then they sat companionably to share the meal; the lamb to remind them of the young lambs that were slaughtered when the Israelites were slaves in Egypt, their blood painted on the door posts so that the angel of God could recognise the houses of God's people; the unleavened bread to remind them of the haste in which they departed and the bitter herbs to remind them of the suffering of their people as they spent years as nomads in the wilderness.

As they ate the meal Jesus looked up at them all and said 'The time is here at last. I so wanted to have this last meal with you all before the end' and he picked up a piece of bread and tore it in halves. His eyes were sad but he managed a smile for them all.

'This is my body!' he said 'Broken for you' and, tearing at it again, began to pass it around to each of the disciples. They took it in silence not quite knowing what to do. John caught his breath and looked in horror at the broken piece of bread in his hands.

Then Jesus leant forward and dipped his bread into the lamb stew and began to eat. He smiled and looked at James 'This is good. Did you make it?'

The tension eased. James laughed 'Mary came up from the house below and showed me what to do' he said. 'And Simon and John did the shopping!'

'It's really good' said Jesus again 'come on everyone. Don't look so sad. This food is too good to waste.'

As the lamb was eaten Jesus turned to Judas who was sitting on his right hand side 'Pass up that pitcher of wine Judas. I think we are ready to drink to the covenant.'

Judas passed the pitcher and Jesus filled his cup and passed the pitcher on. Soon everyone had a cup of wine and they each raised the cup as Jesus spoke. 'In memory of the covenant Moses made for us on Mount Horeb where God promised that he would be our God and we promised that we would be his people. That covenant, sealed with blood and founded on law we remember tonight and with the whole of Israel we pledge ourselves anew.'

'The Covenant!' they all repeated solemnly and lifting their cups drank deep of the sweet red wine.

There was a pause and then Jesus lifted the pitcher again and refilled his cup. 'And this!' he said holding up the cup 'This is my blood of the new covenant shed for all mankind and founded not on laws but on love.' He took a drink from the cup and passed it on to John on his left. 'Drink this, all of you' he said 'and share with me in this cup of suffering and love.'

The cup was passed slowly round the table. Each person taking a nervous sip of the wine, their eyes watching Jesus with apprehension and mounting fear.

As Judas finally passed the cup back, Jesus leant back on the cushions 'When I am gone' he said to them all 'Remember me when you break bread and drink wine together. Remember me with love and I will be there among you. Even if only two or three of you are gathered together I will be there in the midst of you.'

Judas was puzzled 'Why are you talking like this?' he said 'We will have many Passover meals together in the years to come. Surely this is a time to be glad not sorrowful. Soon the Kingdom will come!'

'Yes Judas! said Jesus with a smile 'My Kingdom is not far away.' Then looking sad he gazed around at his disciples 'I have chosen you all with great care' he said 'and you have come a long way but the way ahead will be hard.' He paused and looking down at his empty cup 'And one of you will betray me!'

'No Jesus!' exclaimed Simon as they all sat upright in their shock 'No! It's not possible. None of us would let you down.'

'One of you' repeated Jesus 'one who has shared this meal tonight will betray me.'

Too shocked to speak they darted anxious glances at one another and then Simon finding his voice again said firmly 'Even if everyone else betrays you I never will!'

Jesus smiled at his impetuous friend 'You may not betray me Simon' he said quietly 'but before this night is over, before the cock crow brings in the morning you will have denied even knowing me. Not once but three times.'

Simon's mouth dropped open in horror and the blood drained from his face.

Jesus turned to Judas 'We are going to Gethsemane now. Go and do what you have to do!'

Excitement gleamed in Judas' eyes and he got up from the table and putting on his sandals hurriedly left the room. The door banged behind him in his haste, startling the others. 'Where's Judas going?' whispered Andrew to John.

'I've no idea' replied John 'but Jesus seems to know all about it.'

Andrew moved closer to John 'Judas has been a bundle of nerves since we've been here in Jerusalem' he said 'I'm worried about him.'

'Don't be!' said John 'Jesus doesn't seem concerned. Trust him! He should know. He even knows what we are thinking most of the time.'

'You're right!' agreed Andrew relaxing 'If Jesus is content there can't be much wrong.'

CHAPTER THIRTY

Peering out through the half opened door downstairs Mark watched them all leave the house and walk quietly down the narrow street. He stood for a while with his bed cloth round his slender form as if trying to decide what to do. His mother was already asleep. If he didn't follow them now he would lose them.

Taking a deep breath and tightening the cloth under his armpits he quickly slipped out and closed the door quietly behind him. Keeping to the deep shadows at the side of the street his nimble feet ran silently over the cobbles until the darkened forms of the disciples appeared ahead.

They couldn't use the Golden Gate at night so they followed the labyrinth of streets down to David's old city and went out through the gate nearest to Siloam. Once outside the wall they turned north again and followed the road underneath the wall until they came to the Jericho road, the road which led up the mount and past the Garden of Gethsemane.

The shadows were oppressive and a slight breeze moved the branches of the olive trees. Every so often the full moon appeared surrounded by a halo of cloud. There were no stars tonight.

Other pilgrims from Galilee were already sleeping as Jesus and his friends found their way to the tree which held their bed rolls. The disciples were tired. It was an emotional time, uncertain, and scary and they felt drained and exhausted. It was too late to light a fire. Other fires were dying down as the pilgrims slept and the disciples were anxious to wrap their blankets around them and sleep. A high wall surrounded the garden and for the first time that day they felt safe.

Jesus spoke quietly to Simon, James and John 'I know you're tired' he said 'but I need to pray and I don't want to be disturbed. Will you watch over me?'

'Of course!' agreed Simon anxiously 'We'll do anything. We'll watch and keep you safe.'

'Thank you!' said Jesus 'I will not go far away' and he left the group and went further into the garden beyond the largest gnarled old olive tree. There he found a boulder and knelt beside it and pulling his cloak over his head he began to pray. Simon, James and John watched in silence. He looked so alone. Simon felt his heart would break as he watched his dearest friend.

The doorway into the garden opened a crack and Mark slipped in and was soon hidden among the bushes.

Alone, Jesus was distressed. Tears rolled down his face and he made no attempt to brush them away. 'My father!' he wept 'The time is nearly come. Soon Judas will come and I will be taken. Forgive him Lord, he is young and zealous. He doesn't know what he is doing. He is blind to many things and I am using him and his blindness. Soon they will come and take me and I will be bound and taken to my death.'

Sobs convulsed his body 'Do I truly have to die? Is it really the only way?' he cried and put his head down on to his arms 'Do I have the strength to face it?' he groaned 'O Lord take this cup from me!'

The peace he sought wouldn't come. He who had walked on air to enter heaven in prayer found no comfort, no release 'My God' he cried 'Don't forsake me now, not when I need you the most!'

Agitated, he got to his feet and went back to Simon. He and the others were fast asleep. Gently nudging the sleeping giant, Jesus chided him 'couldn't you stay awake, my rock? I need you now more than ever. Try and stay awake a little longer!'

Simon groaned 'I'm so sorry' he said 'I meant to keep awake.' He pulled himself up and shook his head violently 'The spirit is willing' he gave a rueful grin 'but the flesh is weak!'

'It won't be long now' said Jesus and walked away again. The Passover moon shone briefly between the branches of the trees and the clouds scurried around it softening the contours of its light.

Jesus went back to the same boulder. Ahead of him he could see the far high wall. The light of the moon shone on the stones. They were uneven, easy to climb. Every one was asleep. For sure Simon had gone back to sleep. No one would see him if he slipped away in the darkness. He did not have to stay. No one would miss him till the morning. By then he could be long gone. As he looked, the light on the wall seemed to beckon him and then he turned and looked again at his sleeping disciples and the sleeping mounds of the other pilgrims. And his heart filled with compassion for them all. He could not abandon them now.

He knew that he had to die so that they need never fear death. He had to die so that they might live, so that the Spirit of God, the great power of love that dwelt within him could be released into the world. There was no other way.

Looking up at the moon sailing high in the sky Jesus knew he had no choice 'Thy way O Lord, not mine, be done!' he said and suddenly a peace filled his heart and he wept again, in relief and gratitude. And there he remained, surrounded by the arms of his father.

Back in the city the excited Judas had eventually found Caiaphas' house. He'd never been there before and it was late and dark. When he reached the great doors in the high wall that surrounded the courtyard he had to knock several times before a servant heard him and the door creaked open.

'I want to speak with Malchus' he said urgently.

'It's late!' grunted the servant turning away.

'No! No! You don't understand' Judas was frantic 'He's waiting for me. It's urgent!'

The servant looked him up and down. 'Come inside the door and wait here' he said sternly. 'I'll go and see if Malchus is still awake!'

It was Malchus himself who returned moments later. 'My dear young man!' he gushed 'I had quite given you up. Do you have news for me?'

'Jesus is in Gethsemane!' Judas was eager 'Just as we planned.'

'There's not a moment to lose' replied Malchus clapping his hands.

Five, or was it six? guards appeared from their post on the wall. 'Lead on!' said Malchus to Judas and turning to the guards 'you men follow me.'

A flicker of alarm appeared in Judas' eyes 'Do we need so many guards?' he asked anxiously.

Malchus chuckled 'We wouldn't want any harm to come to your master now would we? Jerusalem is a dangerous place at night. It's better to be safe than sorry.'

Judas nodded. Perhaps Malchus was right.

They hurried down through the streets. The guards clattered a bit as they ran and several heads peered out of doors and seeing the High Priest's guards out and moving with such determination they quickly closed the doors again and went back to bed.

Reaching the Kidron Valley and joining the Jericho road, Malchus caught Judas by the arm. 'How will I recognise Jesus in the dark?' he asked 'I don't want to make a fuss of the wrong man.'

Judas was ready with an answer 'I've thought of that' he said 'I'll go ahead and seek him out and when I find him I will greet him as I always do, with a kiss. Then I will introduce you!'

'Ideal!' said Malchus 'You have the mind of a statesman. You will surely have a great position when your Master comes to power!'

Judas nearly burst with pride. 'Here's the door to the garden' he said at last 'we'll go quietly so as not to wake everyone.'

'Very sensible' agreed Malchus and beckoned the guards in through the door. They followed Judas quietly enough and Judas led them towards the tree where the disciples slept. Jesus did not seem to be there and then suddenly as the moon came out once more Judas saw Jesus standing alone by the boulders at the far end of the garden. He ran eagerly towards him and putting out his hands to touch Jesus' shoulders leant forward to kiss him on the cheek.

Jesus did not protest but as Judas drew away Jesus said quietly 'Do you betray me with a kiss Judas?'

'Betray you?' gasped Judas 'What do you mean?'

Suddenly from behind him he was aware of running feet. 'Hold him fast!' came the harsh voice of Malchus 'Don't let him go!'

Jesus looked up at Malchus 'Day after day I sat teaching in the Temple and you did not lay a hand on me, but here under cover of darkness you have come after me as though I were a bandit.'

'Seize the man!' demanded Malchus raising his voice in anger.

'What's happening?' cried Judas in amazed horror 'Aren't we taking him to Caiaphas as we planned?'

'Oh he's going to Caiaphas alright!' laughed Malchus 'Only not as an honoured guest. He's going as a prisoner!'

A roar of rage burst from the shadows and Simon broke in to the clearing. He brandished the cooking knife he and James had used earlier. He was too angry to stop. He flew at Malchus and slashed with the knife.

Jumping aside Malchus didn't move quickly enough and he howled with pain as the knife slashed at his ear. There was blood everywhere and the ear hung precariously, attached only by a small piece of flesh.

Jesus stepped forward. 'Put away the knife Simon!' and as Simon hesitated Jesus turned towards him sternly 'Do it now!' he repeated.

Simon dropped his hand, still looking thunderous and Jesus stepped forward to Malchus and taking the hanging ear gently in his hand he held it in place for a moment and then stepped away and held out his hands to one of the guards.

Disconcerted for a moment the usually pompous Malchus felt for his ear. It was still there and the blood had stopped. He glared at Jesus 'Bind him!' he said to the guard.

'You can't do this!' protested Judas rushing forward and clutching at Malchus' robes. 'We made plans!'

'We certainly did' agreed Malchus with a smile 'And I'm very grateful. Come and see me later and we'll settle up!'

Simon whirled round and holding up the knife again lunged towards Judas. 'What have you done?' he roared.

'I don't know!' cried Judas his face white and his voice shaking 'I don't know!'

'Take him away!' ordered Malchus to the guard holding Jesus. 'The rest of you can round up some of the others!'

He walked over to Judas who had sunk to the ground 'Not this one though. He's on our side!'

Simon turned on his heels and ran. Hiding in the shadows the other disciples melted back out of sight. Only Judas remained alone.

As Jesus was led away a flash of white cloth caught the eye of one of the guards and he bounded forward and caught hold of the cloth. Wriggling free, Mark sprinted away naked while the guards gave a shout of laughter and, closing ranks around their prisoner, marched briskly towards the city.

CHAPTER THIRTY ONE

The sound of their marching feet and their sharp bursts of laughter seemed to hang in the air for ever and the frightened disciples hid trembling in the shadow of the trees.

Judas alone stayed where he had collapsed and the moon, sailing high, bathed him in light. Too shocked even to cry he knelt there in horror and disbelief.

The sounds of the guards faded away in the distance and one by one the disciples came out and stood by Judas. Fear clutched at their hearts. Simon was the last to join them, his anger and fear plain to see.

He strode over to Judas and roughly catching hold of his tunic lifted him to his feet. 'Where have they taken him?' he shouted.

Judas, startled out of his despair, couldn't speak. His eyes rolled in fear.

'Where?' demanded Simon again 'Where?'

'To Caiaphas' house' stuttered Judas 'that was the plan!'

'Plan!' shouted Simon 'You made a plan with that filthy pig?'

Judas just stared in horror into Simon's face and in irritation Simon flung him to the ground where Judas curled up as small as he could and lay there whimpering like a child.

It was all Simon could do to stop himself kicking him and he looked down at Judas in disgust. 'He said one of us would betray him!' he sneered 'And you proved him right!'

John pushed himself forward. 'Stop it Simon!' he ordered 'Jesus knew about the plan!'

'Knew about it?' shouted Simon incredulous.

'Yes!' said John firmly 'Not only knew about it but told Judas to get on with it. I heard him!'

Stopped in his tracks Simon gulped back his surprise. 'But if he knew about it then he was duped like this fool' he said warily 'I can't believe that. Jesus would have known it was a trick.'

'Jesus did know of the plan' interrupted Andrew 'I heard him speak to Judas too.'

Simon scratched his head. 'I really can't believe that Jesus would allow himself to be duped like this. It doesn't make sense!'

'One of us should tell Lazarus and the women' said Matthew 'and Joseph his uncle needs to know.'

Simon shook his head as if to clear away the horror. 'Do it Matthew! You go to Joseph!' and turning to John and Andrew 'You youngsters go to Bethany.'

He looked down at Judas and with a sigh reached down and took the young man by the hand gently pulling him to his feet 'Seventy times seven he told us. It sounded fine at the time but he never said how hard it would be!'

Brushing the dirt from Judas' clothes, Simon looked him up and down. 'You and I are going to Caiaphas' house to see if we can undo this terrible thing.'

Relief flared briefly in Judas' eyes. Perhaps there was something he could do. Yes! It was all a misunderstanding!

He reached out to Simon and grasped his arm 'Let's go!' he said eagerly 'I know the way. Hurry!'

It seemed to take forever to reach Caiaphas' house on the high ridge inside the city and reaching the doorway Judas knocked impatiently, his fear forgotten. The servant came grumbling to the door and looked bleakly at Judas 'Oh!' he said 'It's you! Malchus said you would come. He's expecting you!' The two men followed the servant into the courtyard.

Although it was late the courtyard seemed a busy place. A brazier flared up in a corner and several servants were standing around it talking. Others scurried about carrying jugs and plates. The six guards lounged around a mounting block and there in the midst of them was Jesus, his hands tied and fastened to the hitching post, standing still while the guards laughed and joked around him.

He looked up as the servant led Judas towards the house. Stopped in his tracks, Simon gazed at his friend in horror. What could he do?

Jesus returned his gaze and Simon was lost in despair. Judas and the servant had disappeared into the house and Simon shrank back again into the shadows of the courtyard watching Jesus, never taking his eyes off his dearest friend.

Inside the building Judas was led into a small room where Malchus stood talking to two of the black robed scribes. He looked up as Judas came in 'Ah! My young friend!' he said with a smile 'You've come for your money no doubt!' and he pulled at the purse on his belt.

'No!' exclaimed Judas 'No I don't want payment!' He looked indignantly at Malchus 'This was not our plan. You told me that Caiaphas was looking forward to meeting Jesus.'

'So he is!' laughed Malchus 'You've done us a great service!' and he stepped forward and clutching hold of Judas' hand, opened his fingers and poured silver coins into his hand. 'Thirty pieces' he said 'this is what we agreed.'

'But Caiaphas was going to help Jesus' stuttered Judas. 'I know he is the Messiah. You can't treat him like this!'

Malchus was dismissive 'Would the Messiah allow himself to be arrested?' he sneered 'Don't talk such rubbish. As for helping him that's the last thing Caiaphas wants to do. Caiaphas needs him out of the way, and fast!'

Then he laughed in Judas' face 'Caiaphas asked me to find the weakest link in Jesus' armour, and I found you!' he laughed again 'You are a fanatic. Your enthusiasm runs away with you. It's easy to tell you things that you want to hear. All fanatics are the same. They think they are strong, they think they are clever but they cannot see how easily they can be manipulated. Because of you, the weakest link in Jesus' chain, we have your master just where we want him!'

Rooted to the spot Judas gasped in horror and disbelief.

Losing patience with him Malchus clapped his hands and a guard appeared from the shadows 'Show him out!' ordered Malchus 'Now!'

The guard stepped towards Judas who did not move. Looking towards Malchus, who briskly nodded his head, the guard then pushed Judas in the chest. 'Come on you!' he growled 'Out!'

Judas turned to Malchus and throwing the coins at his feet shouted 'You have the money! It's blood money. I won't touch it!' and then with the guard unceremoniously pushing him from behind he turned and left the room.

Malchus bent to retrieve the coins. 'Indeed it is blood money' he said with satisfaction 'He is quite right.'

Out in the courtyard again Simon stepped forward eagerly as Judas emerged but Judas signalled him back. Retreating once again into the shadows Simon watched as the guard pushed Judas out through the door into the street beyond.

Despair filling his heart once more, Simon looked across the courtyard to where Jesus was held. Straining his eyes to see how Jesus was coping Simon was surprised to see that Jesus' face was calm and there seemed to be a half smile on his face. He had seen Jesus look like this before. 'On Mount Tabor' he muttered to himself 'when he was talking to Moses and Elijah!'

Jesus turned and looked into the shadows that hid Simon and gave a slight nod. Simon felt tears fill his eyes. Jesus was his friend and he didn't know what to do to help him. He felt so useless, so afraid. Why did Jesus just stand there? Why didn't he use his power and break free?

Just then a servant girl carrying water pushed past him. She was startled at finding someone in the shadows and jumped back in alarm. Some of the water splashed on to Simon's cloak. Instantly the girl apologised 'Come over to the fire and dry your cloak' she urged and when Simon held back she chuckled 'Who ever it is you're waiting for will surely see you in the fire light when he comes out.'

Simon followed her to the fire and in an attempt to be casual began a conversation about the weather. She didn't listen but looked at him puzzled 'You've got a Galilean accent' she said eventually and she looked across at Jesus 'He's from Galilee too. Are you anything to do with him?'

Simon felt the fear knot his stomach 'No!' he exclaimed 'Of course not!'

The girl looked at him curiously 'Why are you so afraid?' she asked 'Is it because he's a terrorist and you think you'll be arrested too? I think you do know him!' she laughed.

'No!' exclaimed Simon again, gazing in horror across the courtyard at Jesus 'No I do not know the man!'

Leaving the fire he began to walk hurriedly towards the door and the girl called over to a group of friends that stood around the entrance. 'I'm sure that man is a friend of the prisoner' she shouted and Simon, cursing loudly, looked at the group of servants and said 'I've no idea what she's talking about!' and with that he pushed them aside and, grasping the door handle, fell out into the street.

Taking to his heels he ran until the could run no more and then, gasping for breath, collapsed on to a step and put his head in his hands. When he lifted his head once more fingers of dawn were lightening the sky and on the wall above him a cock crew.

A stab of pain twisted in his heart and tears rolled down his face

Down in the Kidron Valley Judas stood alone. Despair washed over him in waves. 'Such a fool!' he muttered to himself contemptuously 'A fool!'

Back in the courtyard the guards were tired and anxious for their bed. 'What are we waiting for?' complained one.

'Caiaphas is trying to assemble the Sanhedrin' replied the sergeant at arms.

'At night?' questioned another 'That's not allowed!'

The sergeant shrugged. He pointed at Jesus 'This guy thinks he's the Messiah' he laughed 'the priests don't need Messiahs around when the feast day comes. It's definitely bad for business!'

'The Messiah!' the men were openly incredulous. 'Why he's not even said a word. You'd think a Messiah would have something to say for himself!'

'He did heal Malchus' ear when that ruffian slashed at it' one of the younger guards interrupted thoughtfully.

'A devilish trick!' exclaimed the sergeant looking over at Jesus 'He's a charlatan, a fraud!'

One of the men jumped up and yanking Jesus' neck cloth from around his neck tied it roughly around his eyes. 'Alright miracle worker, let's play a game' he said and he beckoned to another of the guards and urged him to slap Jesus hard. 'Tell us which one hit you!'

The men laughed and getting to their feet eagerly crowded around. Jesus remained silent and another of the guards jabbed him roughly with the end of his staff knocking him off balance.

'That's enough of that!' a hard voice shouted from the doorway to the house. Malchus had appeared again 'Bring him here! We're ready for him!'

As Jesus was led in to the main room of the house he looked around him with interest. The room was high ceilinged and circular in appearance. Ahead of him as he entered, on a small balcony, sat Caiaphas, flanked on his right by his father in law Annas. Other members of the Council, rubbing sleep from their eyes, sat on high backed chairs around the room. In front of the balcony in the limestone floor there was a hole with steps leading down into darkness. A grill stood propped against the wall.

'Is this the man?' sneered Annas, looking with contempt at Jesus. 'He doesn't look too much of a threat!'

'Looks can be deceiving!' snapped Caiaphas and nodded to Malchus 'Bring in the witnesses' he ordered.

A worried frown crossed Malchus' face. Even though he'd had several days to plan this moment, he had failed to find really convincing witnesses, and he knew it.

One by one the witnesses were brought in and made their accusations. 'He tells people not to pay the Temple tax' said one 'No it was the interest charged by the money lenders that he objected to' stated another. 'He doesn't pay the tax himself' said one 'Yes I saw him doing it' said another. 'I've heard that he's going to knock the Temple down.' 'He was talking about a distant future. Like a prophet' another objected.

The few Council members that were present did their best to make sense of the wild accusations and Caiaphas raised his eyebrows at Malchus to show his displeasure.

Surely he had better witnesses than these. It was necessary to get at least two witnesses to agree about something. Finally two men did agree that they heard Jesus say that he would pull down the Temple and rebuild it in three days.

Nicodemus got to his feet 'that can't be taken literally,' he said 'if Jesus did say it at least have the courtesy to ask him what he meant by it.'

The High Priest looked at Jesus 'Well?' he asked.

Jesus made no reply.

'Have you no answer to these allegations?' spluttered Caiaphas, irritated by Jesus' calm demeanour.

Still Jesus stood in silence.

In agitation Caiaphas took his staff and banged it violently on the balustrade in front of him. 'By the living God!' he shouted 'Are you the Messiah, the Son of God or not?'

And Jesus looking up directly into Caiaphas' eyes said quietly 'I am!'

A gasp rippled around the room and Jesus spoke up again 'I tell you this' he said firmly and with such authority that the Council members fell silent 'from this moment on you will see the Son of Man seated at the right hand of the Almighty and coming on the clouds of Heaven.'

The silence continued and then Caiaphas stood up and solemnly tore his silk tabard from top to bottom. 'This is blasphemy!' he exclaimed 'You have all heard him. What need have we of further witnesses.' He looked triumphantly around 'What is your verdict?'

'He should die' shouted Malchus.

'Yes!' the Council members agreed. 'He should die!'

Nicodemus stood, his face white and his old hands shaking 'No!' he shouted 'You cannot pass judgement. This court is illegal! Our own laws tell us that we cannot try a man for a capital offence under the cover of darkness. We also must hold a proper meeting in the Council chamber, not in a private house. And an accused man cannot condemn himself. Witnesses must agree!'

Caiaphas glared at him 'Don't you see how dangerous this man is? We can't delay any longer.'

'It must be done according to our law!' persisted Nicodemus and some of the elder Council members began nodding their heads in agreement.

'Very well then!' snapped Caiaphas. 'Have it your own way. This court is adjourned until the first hour. Go to your homes. You have three hours to sleep. We will meet again in day light in the Council Chambers.'

The members groaned.

'You can thank Nicodemus for this' Caiaphas was livid. 'But as for witnesses' he looked down at Malchus 'don't bother' he snarled. 'We have all been witnesses tonight. We don't need anyone else.'

Then looking at where Jesus stood quietly watching him he barked at the guards and pointed to the cell entrance 'Put him down. We'll see if he's still as arrogant in the morning!'

CHAPTER THIRTY TWO

The cell was dark and cold. They gave him no light and he felt the walls with his bare hands. They were solid stone carved out by small axes. A water cistern he surmised. No way out.

'I am shut in with no escape. Darkness is my only companion,' he quoted from the Psalms 'O Lord, my God. Let my prayer come before you!'

He knelt on the stone floor and pulled his cloak over his head. Did angels come and minister to him during those dark morning hours? The guards discussed it among themselves for many a day afterwards.

Three long hours later when they bustled down to drag Jesus out they expected to find him shivering from cold and cowed in despair. Instead there was a peacefulness about this man and a strange sense of luminosity. It was almost as though he had been dipped in God and new created.

Jesus walked calmly from the cell and, looking at the morning sun with a sense of wonder in his eyes, he held his head high and walked out with the guards, down the road to the Council buildings on the south wall of the Temple.

The guard flanked him closely but they needn't have worried; the streets were still deserted. The Council meeting was just a formality. It was obvious that the decision had already been made.

Jesus did not speak.

Caiaphas was anxious 'We need to get Pilate to ratify our decision' he pressed. 'Sunset brings in the festival. We don't have much time!'

Old Annas spoke up 'Pilate will not be impressed with a blasphemy charge. He's not interested in our religion.'

Malchus stepped towards the dais 'The business with the taxes should do it' he offered 'and his talk of a Kingdom.'

He looked around at the Council 'A kingdom implies a king. Caesar cannot tolerate another king.'

Caiaphas nodded his head thoughtfully 'Yes!' he agreed 'Taxes and claiming to be a king should be enough.'

'The witnesses didn't agree about the taxes!' said Nicodemus to the full Council 'In fact none of them agreed about anything!'

Caiaphas shrugged 'The Council is closed!' he said and he looked down on Malchus. 'Let's get this over and done with. Get this man to Pilate as quickly as we can.'

Leaving the Council chamber the guard marched Jesus through the outer court of the Temple towards the Sheep Gate. Stall holders were setting up their stalls and stopped to stare as the guards marched passed. Caiaphas and Annas followed at a more dignified pace and surrounded by the Council members.

It was early but pilgrims had already started arriving in the Temple. They too stopped and stared as the little procession hurried through.

Lazarus, flanked by the women and Jesus' brothers, was anxiously entering the courtyard through the Golden Gate. Seeing Jesus surrounded by the guard the group froze in its tracks their eyes wide with horror. John and Andrew following on through the gate halted behind the others. Jesus didn't see them but Nicodemus limping on behind left the other Council members and hurried to their side. His distress was obvious. 'They've got him Lazarus!' he wailed 'I couldn't stop them. I tried but they wouldn't listen!'

Lazarus stepped forward to catch the old man as he stumbled and as he did so Jesus' mother caught him by the hands. 'My son?' she urged Nicodemus 'Where are they taking him?'

'Oh dear lady!' Nicodemus was close to tears 'They're taking him to Pilate. They want the death penalty.'

Mary gasped and put her hand to her throat.

'What can we do?' she whispered.

Nicodemus hesitated and then in a firmer voice he said 'He needs friends. One voice, mine, was not enough. He needs many more, friends that can be heard.' He drew a deep breath 'Where are all his supporters?' he asked looking around.

'Most are still asleep. They have no idea what has happened' said Mary in despair.

'Get his disciples to round up as many as they can and bring them quickly to the Antonia. There isn't much time.' Nicodemus caught his breath 'They mean to kill him' he gasped 'hurry now!'

***

Pilate was annoyed at being summoned so early in the morning. He had no time for priests and the Passover was nothing but an aggravation. He grumbled as he strode along to the corridor to the open court. 'Well!' he said tersely to Caiaphas 'What do you want!'

Caiaphas pulled himself up and pointed at Jesus 'We want you to try this man' he demanded imperiously.

'Try him yourself!' snapped Pilate 'You have the power. Don't waste my time!' and he turned to go back inside.

'We don't have the power to sentence him to death' said Caiaphas with a hint of petulance. 'You took that power away from us!'

'The death sentence!' Pilate was incredulous. He looked at Jesus standing calmly in front of him 'Why? What on earth can a man like this have done to deserve death? What evil has he done?'

Caiaphas drew a sharp breath 'This man is an agitator, a trouble maker, he is subverting our nation. He teaches people not to pay their taxes and he claims to be the Messiah, a king!'

Pilate looked amazed. He raised an eyebrow at Jesus 'Well?' he asked.

Jesus remained silent.

Pilate tried again. 'Don't you hear what they are saying about you? Won't you say anything in your defence?'

Still Jesus did not speak and Pilate began to feel anxious. There was something about this man's eyes and the way he looked at you. 'Are you a king?' he asked more respectfully. 'Are you the King of the Jews?'

'That is not a term I would use' said Jesus 'King is your word not mine. My Kingdom is not of this world. If it were my followers would be fighting for my freedom. No, my Kingdom is in Heaven!'

Pilate eyed him carefully. He was certainly a cool customer but not dangerous, he thought, although he could see why Caiaphas would not like him. He turned to Caiaphas 'I find no case against this man!' he said firmly.

Caiaphas was furious 'His teaching is causing unrest among all the people in the land. It started in Galilee and now has spread here!' he shouted angrily.

Pilate smiled 'Ah!' he said 'Let's see what Herod Antipas has to say about the matter. If this man is a Galilean Herod must have a say!' He turned to an aide 'Is Herod in the city yet?' he asked.

'He arrived yesterday sir' the aide replied.

'There we are then' beamed Pilate 'take him to Herod!' and he turned on his heels and went back inside for his breakfast.

Caiaphas was so angry he could barely speak. 'He knows we have to do this before the sun goes down' he spluttered. 'He's using delaying tactics to upset me.' He stamped towards the courtyard doors gesticulating to the guards 'Hurry up! We don't have much time!' and he turned to Malchus 'you left all this far too late' he snarled 'I don't need all this stress!'

The streets were already filling up with people as the guards clattered their way up the shallow steps of the streets towards Herod's palace. Annas was red in the face with exertion but determined to be there in case his fool son in law didn't get the result he needed.

Nicodemus sat on the wall outside the Antonia where Mary found him. 'Pilate's bought us more time!' said Nicodemus. 'It will be a good hour before they get back from Herod.'

Mary breathed a sigh of relief 'The crowds from the Mount should be here by then' she said.

Nicodemus gave her a warning look 'Don't think Malchus won't be doing the same' he said 'I've seen his scouts already out touting for support. They want this over quickly so he's rallying his mob!'

Blood drained from Mary's face. 'Do you think there's any hope?' she asked piteously.

Nicodemus patted her arm 'There's always hope!' he said.

***

When Herod head that Caiaphas had brought Jesus to him he was delighted. Ever since the death of John the Baptist he had had sleepless nights. He'd heard of Jesus, of course. He'd even entertained the thought that Jesus was John the Baptist come back to haunt him and he welcomed a chance to see this holy man for himself.

Herod strode quickly into the anteroom and his eyes fell on the still figure of Jesus immediately. His out-take of breath was the only indication of his relief. This was certainly not John the Baptist. He addressed Jesus with respect and Caiaphas scowled as he proceeded to ask Jesus questions.

But Jesus would not reply. He stood calmly watching his cousin's murderer until he eventually ran out of words.

Herod was disappointed. He'd heard about the miracles and he wanted to see one performed but Jesus was obviously not going to please him in that way. He was also embarrassed. How could this man remain so unmoved when spoken to by his Tetrarch?

Caiaphas moved alongside Herod 'He thinks he's more important than you' he spoke softly 'he says he's a king!'

Herod laughed with relief 'Oh!' he said 'He's a lunatic. That explains it all' and he bowed in Jesus' direction 'Your majesty!' he exclaimed. Then turning to his attendants he said 'Give him a robe more suited for a king.'

When they returned they dressed Jesus in a purple robe and while he stood in silence he was mocked and ridiculed by them all. Then Herod held up his hand 'Take him back to Pilate' he ordered. 'I can have nothing to do with sentencing a lunatic to death and, if he is not a lunatic, then he is after all a holy man. I've killed one holy man. I'm certainly not going to have another on my conscience!'

Caiaphas groaned with frustration 'More delay!' he muttered 'and this is my busiest day!'

He turned on the guards 'Take him back!' he shouted 'And quickly!'

Back at the Antonia the court was filling with the crowds and as Jesus was brought back in a sigh of despair echoed around the open yard.

Caiaphas scowled at Malchus who spread out his hands as if to say "there's nothing I can do!"

Summoned again Pilate strode out on to the balcony. 'Herod finds no fault with this man' he declared 'and neither do I' he looked at Caiaphas 'I propose that he is flogged and then released. That should be enough!' The crowd gasped and Caiaphas looked as if he would explode with anger but before he could protest Pilate had beckoned to his soldiers. They came at a run and surrounded Jesus, bearing him off into the drill yard adjacent to the court.

The crowd fell silent and as the whip whistled through the air tears began to fall. Several of the people from Galilee were physically sick and some, held back by friends, were all for challenging the might of the great Roman Empire there and then.

Everybody waited.

When Jesus emerged he was being dragged by the soldiers and the crowd gasped again to see the open weals on his back and his hair and clothes so spattered with blood.

'Now he is to be released' said Pilate turning to the soldiers 'See to it!'

'No!' came a roar from the centre of the crowd. 'Crucify him! Crucify him!' they shouted. Caiaphas turned to Malchus with a smile. 'That's more like it' he said 'Well done' he said with a smile.

'It's costing us!' replied Malchus anxiously.

'Anything!' agreed Caiaphas raising a hand to encourage the crowd.

'Crucify him!' cried the crowd again.

But this time the Galileans made themselves heard 'Let him go!' they cried 'He's innocent!'

Pilate looked confused and the crowds shouted all the more. Some of the officers came to stand alongside Pilate. 'Why not let him go as the Festival pardon' said one.

Mightily relieved Pilate stepped forward and lifted his hand and the crowd fell silent again. 'It is my custom to free a prisoner of your choice at Passover times so I propose to free this Jesus' he said. The crowd remained silent as they took this news in. then as the Galileans began to cheer with relief one of the group in the middle of the yard shouted up to Pilate 'He is not our choice! The custom is that it is our choice!' he declared.

Pilate was non-plussed 'Who do you choose then?' he asked and the man bent to confer with his companions.

'We choose Barabbas' he cried when he stood straight again.

A gasp of disbelief ran around the yard. Even Pilate was shocked. 'Barabbas is a murderer' he protested and he pointed to Jesus 'and this man has done no wrong.'

'He called himself a king' interrupted Caiaphas.

Pilate groaned 'We'll let the crowd decide then' he agreed. 'Who shall I release this Passover?' he shouted 'Jesus Barabbas or Jesus who calls himself King?'

The men gathered in the centre roared their answer 'Give us Barabbas!' they cried.

'What then should I do with this man?' Pilate asked.

'Crucify him!' they chanted and the roar was deafening. 'Crucify him!'

The "No!" of the Galileans could not be heard neither could the crying of the women.

Pilate scowled at Caiaphas 'You've bribed the crowd' he said and he pointed at Jesus 'this man is innocent.'

Caiaphas scowled back and spoke menacingly 'If you let this man go' he said 'you are not Caesar's friend.'

Pilate was shocked. Complaints had gone to Caesar about him before. He knew he would be in serious trouble if Caiaphas sent a formal complaint. He flushed in frustration and turned to his officers 'Crucify him!'

he conceded sulkily and then beckoning to his aide he took a stylus and inscribed the document "Jesus of Nazareth, The King of the Jews" and went to give it to the commander of the guard.

His face dark with anger Caiaphas moved to stop him 'You can't write that. It is an insult to our nation' he exclaimed. 'Change it!' he demanded.

Pilate said nothing.

'Change it!' repeated Caiaphas. Write "he said he was the King of the Jews."

Pilate grimaced 'Take it or leave it' he said 'what I have written I have written and you must be content!'

This small victory made him smile as he walked away. It was enough for now, he thought, but there would come a time when he would pay Caiaphas back for this humiliation. Caiaphas would be sorry.

CHAPTER THIRTY THREE

'No!' The shout from the Galileans was shrill with despair. It echoed around the courtyard and then petered out into a gasping silence. They gazed, open mouthed in horror, as Jesus was pushed ahead of the soldiers, through the archway, into the flagstone yard of Antonia's prison and out of sight.

'No!' whispered Mary sinking slowly to the ground, her face ashen with terror. John rushed forward and, picking her up, led her to the wall away from the jostling crowd.

Ciaiphas' paid mob was loudly congratulating itself and Malchus was unashamedly handing out coins. Caiaphas himself hurried from the court. Now the Passover celebrations were his sole concern.

Mary clung to John for support 'Oh John!' she cried 'Did you see his poor back? How can he still stand?'

John held her still 'He has an inner strength' he said 'you, as his mother, must know that!'

'I do!' she wept 'But how I wish he would use that strength to help himself! Even now he could stop all this if he had a mind to.'

'I remember him telling us that the way of love would be hard' John thought back to when Jesus had asked him to be a disciple 'I never imagined just how hard!'

'Is there anything at all we can do?' Mary looked round desperately. 'Where's Simon? Where are the others?'

'I don't know!' panicked John 'We all became separated last night.' He looked around 'Perhaps they are here in the crowd somewhere. It so early most of the pilgrims haven't got into the Temple yet. They don't know what's happening.'

Andrew pushed through the crowd towards them 'Look' he said 'more Galileans are arriving! And there's your James!'

Looking flustered James came rushing forward 'Mother' he cried 'what's happening? Where's Jesus? There are all sorts of rumours going around.'

Just then a loud jeer from the mob made them look up sharply and the colour drained from James' face. Jesus appeared silhouetted in the archway. He was wearing Herod's purple cloak and on his head the soldiers had jammed a twisted crown of thorns.

'Hail King of the Jews!' mocked the soldiers and made elaborated bows before him.

The crowd laughed and Malchus angrily stepped forward to the centurion. 'Take those things off him!' he demanded 'It's an insult to our nation to call him our King!'

The centurion contemptuously pushed Malchus back and stepped forward to Jesus prodding him with his staff. 'Come on King!' he said 'Move!' and Jesus stumbled forward.

Flushed with anger Malchus lunged forward and grabbed at the cloak as Jesus was hustled forward. The fastening snapped and the cloak came away in his hands and the crowd gasped as they saw the livid weals, open and bleeding across Jesus' back.

Two other prisoners were pushed out after Jesus. When they saw the crowd they began shouting, protesting their innocence. Then as they were pushed by the soldiers towards the gateway to the road they started to curse.

Jesus walked ahead in silence.

'We must stay with him!' exclaimed Mary and began pushing her way frantically through the crowd.

James caught her arm 'You'll never get close to him that way' he said 'Come! I'll show you!' and he led her quickly down a narrow passage. John, Andrew and Lazarus and the women followed nervously. It didn't take long. Within minutes they were out in the street well ahead of the crowds.

'He will pass here!' said James 'Make sure the crowds don't push you back when they come. Fight to keep your place!'

A cohort of soldiers marched ahead of the condemned men. Wielding staves they pushed onlookers hard against the wall. James sprang in front of his mother to protect her and received a violent jab in the shoulder whirling him off balance.

'Keep out of the way!' growled the soldier marching on without breaking his stride but James, recovering, swung round and, as the milling crowd stormed down the narrow streets alongside the prisoners, pushed his mother forward again and steadied her against the crush.

Carrying his own cross bar Jesus came next. He was weighed down by its weight and the jolting of the rough wood on his bare shoulder had caused the weals to split open. Blood trickled down his face from the sharp thorns which jabbed into his head and mingled with the sweat of exertion.

Even so, his eyes were still calm and he put one foot in front of the other as though he were living a dream.

'Jesus!' whispered Mary through her tears.

Jesus' eyes searched the crowds and came to rest on his group of friends and he smiled. 'Mother!' he said and looked deep into her eyes.

'I am here son' she whispered again 'I won't leave you' and she began to move with the crowd keeping pace with Jesus.

'My father is with me!' his eyes flickered and John caught his breath. Jesus paused with the effort of walking. 'I am quite safe' he said eventually 'don't be afraid for me!'

John caught Andrew's arm 'Just for a moment' he gasped 'Jesus looked like he always did when he went to prayer.'

'Walking to heaven on air,' agreed Andrew.

'But he must be in so much pain' John was sobbing as he ran with the excited crowds.

'Too much pain to feel' grunted James lunging forward to stop his mother falling on the uneven cobble stones.

The other Mary pushed her way forward and caught hold of Mary's arm. She looked up at James 'We'll hold her between us!' she said firmly.

The narrow street wound upwards out of the town and then the little procession and its excited crowds suddenly spilled out into the sunlight beyond the walls. When the other prisoners saw ahead of them the upright posts wedged into the rocks they began to curse and scream with fear.

'Too late for all of that!' grunted the centurion 'But it livens things up for the crowd. A crucifixion is not much fun if the prisoners don't protest!' He looked quizzically at Jesus 'Can't make this one out. He hasn't made any noise at all!'

'He will in a minute!' grinned one of the soldiers grabbing a bucket of nails. 'Bring him over here!' he called to the others 'We'll start with him.'

Seizing the cross bar and throwing it down the men roughly pushed Jesus to the ground and dragged him so that his arms lay along the bar.

In a swift practiced movement the soldier put his knee across Jesus' arm and pinned it to the bar. One of the others grabbed Jesus' hand and held it fast.

The large nail was jabbed violently in to the wrist and three sharp knocks with the hammer drove it through the flesh and bone and into the wood.

Jesus gasped and his eyes flew open with the pain. When they grabbed the other arm he looked up at the soldiers and between blows spoke haltingly 'Father!' he cried 'Forgive them! They don't know what they're doing.'

The men laughed 'I think we do!' said one 'It's you that seems not to know. What world do you live in, anyway?'

The centurion looked down at Jesus and a frown wrinkled his brow 'He certainly is a strange one' he said. Then pulling himself together he turned to his men 'Get on with it. The quicker this job's done the better!'

One by one the three men were raised on their cross bars to the top of the posts. Then the soldiers grabbed the hanging legs and bending them up lashed the ankles to the post and hammered home another large nail.

'That's it!' said the centurion thankfully and he turned to his officers 'Deploy the men to keep the crowds back. We have to stay with this lot until they die.'

The men groaned 'That could be days!' moaned one.

'No' said the centurion 'it's their High Sabbath tonight. We must have them dead and off the crosses before sun down!'

A howl of dismay reached their ears and the crowd suddenly surged forward. The soldiers rushed to hold them back and keep control. Still there were loud cries and the crowd heaved again. 'It's that lot over there!' said one of the soldiers pointing and the centurion looked, scrutinising the group and trying to assess the danger.

'They look like Galileans' he said at last 'big fellows, country bumpkins. What's got into them?'

'That man is from Galilee' said on officer pointing at Jesus.

The centurion beckoned him over 'Go and find out what their trouble is' he ordered 'and be quick!'

The officer strode over to the gesticulating crowd and when he came back he looked as if he was trying to stifle a laugh. He pointed to Jesus again 'They say that man is their leader' he said grinning 'he's the expected Messiah!'

The soldiers laughed.

'Some even said they believed him to be the Son of God' the officer was openly chuckling now.

'They should have looked after him better if he was so important to them.' The centurion was impatient.

'They've only just heard what has happened' the officer explained 'as you know the Galileans always camp on the Mount of Olives during Passover. It seems this man was arrested, tried and sentenced before most of them woke this morning.'

The centurion looked thoughtful 'There's something very odd about this' he said looking up at Jesus again. 'He doesn't seem like a criminal.' Turning to the other officer he said 'Was there a special order with that one?'

'There's this!' said another, bringing forward Pilate's scribbled note. He looked at it and grinned 'It says "Jesus of Nazareth. The King of the Jews".'

The centurion looked grim 'Even Pilate's having a joke' he said and he pointed to the man. 'Nail this on his cross!' he ordered and he watched glumly as the man hurried to do his bidding.

'What shall we do about the crowds?' asked the officer anxiously 'They're very upset.'

'Keep them back' growled the centurion 'the hot sun will wear them down. Only let close family members through!'

Among the new comers were the rest of the disciples. Seeing Mary with Lazarus and the others in the front of the crowd they edged their way forward until they too reached the front. Eyes shaded by guilt and horror they stood aghast at the sight of Jesus. Simon and Judas stood back. Their faces white with shock with tears running unchecked down their cheeks. James looked at them anxiously. 'You are right to be afraid' he whispered to Thomas. 'Jesus has been sentenced for insurrection. If you are seen to be his followers you could be in danger too. Hide in the crowd but don't be seen as a group or questions will be asked.' He looked back at Thomas 'Get hold of Simon and take him away. He's far too obvious!' Giving Thomas a gentle push he repeated 'Go on! Move!'

It took a few minutes for the danger to sink in but when James turned round again the disciples all melted into the crowd.

Mary looked up at James 'Do you think your uncle Joseph could do anything!' she begged.

James' eyes lit up 'Why didn't I think of that! There's still a chance! He could still live!' he hugged her in relief 'I'll go now. He'll know what to do!'

As James sped away Jesus lifted his head and looked down at his mother. Seeing the look the soldier nearest to her stood forward 'Are you a relative?'

John spoke up 'She's his mother.'

'And you?' asked the soldier.

'His cousin!'

'You can go up and speak to him if you wish.'

Mary turned and clutched at John's arm 'Come!' she said tugging him forward.

The crowd hushed as they saw what was happening and Mary and John stumbled over the stony ground to the foot of the cross. 'Jesus! My dear son' wept Mary and the tears ran down her face 'what have they done to you?'

'Master!' cried John and the two of them clung together in their distress.

A look of utmost compassion came into Jesus' eyes 'I told you not to be fearful!' he said. 'Don't be concerned for me. You should be concerned for yourselves! I cannot stay to look after you both so you must look after each other.'

'Love each other!' he continued sadly 'There's not enough love in the world, that's why things like this can happen. But be patient and you will see that love will conquer all!'

John began to sob hysterically 'How are we to live without you?' he cried.

'Those that there is love between can never be separated' said Jesus 'Just remember me with love and I will be there. I will never leave you!'

His voice became tired. 'It's nearly time' he said weakly.

'That's enough!' said the soldier gruffly 'Get back now!'

As John led Mary away a group of women were allowed through with a bucket of wine and water. 'Give them all something to drink!' ordered the soldier and the women dipped their sponges into the wine and held it up to the prisoners on the end of long sticks. The two men on either side of Jesus drank eagerly but when the sponge touched Jesus' lips it tasted strange and the woman said 'Drink it! There is a drug in the wine that will ease the pain! Drink!'

Jesus turned his head aside 'I won't drink now' he said 'I will wait and drink it anew in the Kingdom!'

'Kingdom!' sneered one of the convicts 'If you're a King why don't you save yourself and us. Why don't you use your famous power?'

'Yes!' chanted some of the crowd glad of a diversion 'You saved others! Why not save yourself?'

'Be quiet!' said the other convict weakly 'Leave him alone! He's suffering as we are and I have a feeling that he's done nothing wrong!'

'Of course he has!' shouted the first 'The Romans might be brutal but they are just!'

Ignoring him the other convict looked intently at Jesus willing him to raise his head.

Jesus looked into his eyes.

'Jesus!' the man said 'Remember me when you come in to your Kingdom!'

Jesus' voice was disembodied. He was fading fast. But he smiled and said 'Today you will be with me in Paradise' and unable to hold it up any longer his head fell on his chest.

The sun beat down on the crowds and the three men on the crosses were silent. Jesus' eyes were closed and the soldiers began to wilt in their leather tunics.

Then Jesus coughed and began to struggle to breath. He tried to pull himself upright to clear his lungs but his legs were bent and he couldn't put any pressure on them. He coughed and began to gasp for breath. 'My God!' he cried 'Don't forsake me now!' and then heaving himself up to gulp in some air he collapsed with the effort and the pain.

The crowd from Galilee began to moan in agony and a wind picked up and whirled the dust around the crosses. James, hurrying back from the city, joined his mother at the front of the crowd. 'Joseph's gone to see Pilate now!' he said.

'It's too late!' said Mary sadly 'Too late!'

Summoning up the last vestiges of his strength Jesus raised his head. The crowd gasped. His eyes were alight and his face infused with joy. 'It is finished!' he shouted in triumph and his head slumped on his chest and he breathed his last.

The wind whirled and tore at the crowd and turning their heads the people lifted their clothing to cover their faces. The sky became black with a darkness that could be felt as the storm blew in from the desert and whipped its way across the city to the countryside beyond.

When it was past the crowd were silent and the centurion walked over to the cross and looked up at Jesus. He looked in bewilderment at the still form and then seeming to make up his mind he shook his head and turned to his officers 'Truly!' he said firmly 'This man was the Son of God.'

CHAPTER THIRTY FOUR

'I must try and stop Joseph' said James anxiously 'Pilate was keeping him waiting in the ante room. I may be able to stop him. He won't want to put himself on the line unnecessarily.'

'Go!' said Mary wearily 'But come back soon. I need you.'

James was wrong. He found Joseph in the ante room still waiting but far from being glad not to have to approach Pilate. The old man was adamant 'I'm not ashamed to stand by Jesus' he said 'he was a fine young man and certainly not a criminal.' He looked determined 'I shall stay and see the man who sent him to his death, and I shall ask him to release my nephew's body for burial.' He stood up and paced around 'I've built a new family tomb' he announced 'Jesus will have the chief place.'

As they waited, Nicodemus hobbled through the door to join them. Joseph looked up pleased 'Good to see you, old friend. We'll go in and face this mad man together.'

'Of course!' Nicodemus readily agreed 'but it was Caiaphas and not Pilate that was to blame for all this.'

'If Pilate wasn't so weak' began Joseph as the door to Pilate's room swung open. Leaving James behind Joseph marched into the room 'We've come to ask you to release the body of Jesus of Nazareth for burial' he demanded.

Pilate swung round on his seat 'Why? He can't be dead already' he said testily.

'He is!' replied Joseph equally curt.

Pilate beckoned to a slave 'Go and find out!' he ordered.

The slave left hurriedly and Pilate turned to Joseph 'Of what interest is this man to you?' he asked.

'He's a nephew' said Joseph 'and a good man.'

Pilate looked away 'Where were you this morning when Caiaphas insisted I make a judgement?' he said plaintively.

'At home' replied Joseph 'By the time decent people were getting up this morning decisions had already been made.' He glared at Pilate. 'Why the unseemly haste?' he continued.

Pilate looked away again 'The Festival' he said 'they wanted everything out of the way before the Passover started.'

'Well!' said Joseph grimly 'They got their way didn't they? With a couple of hours to spare!'

The slave slipped back in to the room and nodded at Pilate 'He's dead!' he said 'But the other two are still alive.'

'Tell the centurion to break their legs' he ordered briskly, getting up out of his seat. 'This whole business has taken too long.'

He turned to Joseph 'Take his body!' He went to the desk and took his pen and scribbled a note. 'Take this to the centurion and take his body!'

He strode to the door and then hesitated and turned back 'its unfortunate all this business' he muttered. 'I've valued your friendship in the past. I hope next time we meet it will be in more pleasant circumstances.' He didn't give Joseph a chance to reply. Turning on his heel he quickly left the room.

The two men took to the streets following the very route Jesus had taken that morning. Shutters on the shops were already closed and people were scurrying to their homes. The start of the festival was less than an hour away.

When they reached the crucifixion site the crowds were gone and the bodies were being taken down from the crosses. Joseph gave the centurion the note and after looking at the old man curiously the centurion said tersely 'Take him!'

John and Andrew stood with Mary and the women and Joseph joined them quickly. 'My tomb is not far' he said to John gasping a little for breath 'Can you two carry him?'

'Of course!' anxious to help they hurried to the body.

Indeed it wasn't very far. A new tomb cut into the rocks, its entrance concealed by a large round stone, stood literally yards away. Together they pushed the stone back and carefully took Jesus into the tomb.

'Over here!' ordered Joseph leading them to the back.

The sinking sun shone its light into the tomb and they could see quite clearly the low cut platform that awaited the head of the household. 'Put him here!' said Joseph 'Cover him and we can come back after the Sabbath to wash the body and wrap it in spices.'

Reverently the women laid a sheet over the body and weeping quietly they filed out of the tomb and the stone was rolled across the entrance.

'Come back to Bethany' said Lazarus 'you too James! We need to be together tonight.'

Taking their leave of Joseph and Nicodemus the sad little group hurried through the now deserted streets to the gate by the Pool of Siloam. Nobody spoke. Everyone was lost in their own thoughts.

It was a shock when they joined the road to Bethany to find a group of the disciples waiting for them in the gathering shadows. Their faces ashen with shock they stood together uncertain what to do.

Mary's hand flew up to her throat 'Has something else happened?' she asked anxiously.

'It's Judas!' said Simon.

'Did they catch him? Was he arrested?' demanded James.

'No!' said Simon miserably 'He's hung himself!' and he sat down on a boulder and put his head in his hands 'And I never told him that I understood.'

'Nor did any of us' said Thomas quietly.

'It might have helped a little if he had known you all forgave him' said Mary wisely 'but I don't think Judas would ever have forgiven himself! At least he knows now that Jesus still loves him.'

'Where's his body?' asked James.

'The authorities cut him down and took it away' mumbled Simon. He got to his feet and looked across the city to the setting sun. Then he pointed to Mark 'Young Mark came to find us,' he said 'we're going to hide out in his mother's house. There's too many of us to stay with you Lazarus. And Malchus is your neighbour. We'll be anonymous in the city.'

The shofars began to wail over the city and Peter looked up at them all 'Now the festival has begun and the powers of evil have won the day' he said glumly. 'There's no sign left of our beloved Master and all our dreams and hopes are dashed. And I am the most despised of men, for I denied my dearest friend.'

Andrew reached out to his brother but Simon shrugged his hand away and with head bent low he turned and trudged back towards the city.

As the sound of the shofars died down Malchus bustled in to Caiaphas' office at the Temple 'There's a rumour going around' his tone was anxious and Caiaphas looked up alarmed.

'They're saying that Jesus of Nazareth is going to rise from the dead!'

'What nonsense!' Caiaphas was dismissive.

'Of course it is' said Malchus soothingly 'but something very strange happened in Bethany. You remember? I was there and Lazarus walked out of the tomb.'

Malchus looked agitated 'It was a trick of course' he added quickly 'but a lot of people believed it.'

Caiaphas rubbed his nose 'Another trick like that and we could have trouble' he agreed. 'It was sensible of you to warn me!'

He got to his feet briskly 'We'll need a guard on that tomb. It wouldn't do if those disciples of his stole his body and let everyone think he had risen from the dead. My God!' he said 'That doesn't bear thinking about. Come on!' For such a large dignified man Caiaphas could move surprisingly quickly.

Pilate could hardly believe his ears 'Rise from the dead?' he roared 'I cannot believe you are taking this seriously!'

Caiaphas flushed 'Of course he won't rise from the dead' he said contemptuously 'if that were truly possible we wouldn't be able to stop it.' He glared at Pilate 'We want to prevent a deception' he insisted. 'If we don't we will all be a laughing stock and this Jesus will be seen to be a god.'

Pilate looked at him soberly 'Yes!' he said 'That's what worries me too.'

Ignoring this comment Caiaphas came quickly to the point 'All we need is for you to send soldiers to guard the tomb' he said persuasively 'three days at the most. Then this problem will go away!'

Pilate sighed 'I doubt it' he said. 'My wife is blaming me for this man's death and has shut herself in her room. Will this trouble never end?'

'The guard?' queried Caiaphas gently.

'Alright! Alright!' Pilate had had enough. He stood up and beckoned to the guard at the door. 'Arrange for the High Priest to have six soldiers!' The guard ran off.

'Get your soldiers from the barrack commander' said Pilate 'you tell them what you want them to do' he made for the door 'I've had enough!'

As the door swung open he banged it petulantly with his fist as he stormed out 'I've certainly had enough!'

CHAPTER THIRTY FIVE

The Passover festival was a subdued event. The usually boisterous Galileans were quiet and went about their religious duties in a perfunctory manner. There was no spontaneous singing. No laughter. They were all eager to leave for home as soon as possible. The authorities were pleased. They had made their money and there were no disturbances. What could be better?

In Bethany the women busied themselves gathering the herbs and spices they needed. They sorted linen into baskets and put everything ready. Nobody spoke very much and the day seemed to drag. No-one slept that night either and it was a good hour before dawn the following day, the first day of the week, when the women began to gather in the darkness outside Lazarus' house. Jesus' mother and Salome were missing.

'Mary has only just now dropped asleep' said Joanna 'Salome will stay with her. She's so exhausted! One of us can take her to the tomb later in the day.'

No fingers of light heralded the new day but the birds had already started to sing as they hurried through the shadows. Pilgrims camping on the Mount were already leaving for the journey home and looked curiously at the little group of women as they hurried past.

Unaware, the women hurried on across the Kidron Valley and in through the gates of the city. The streets were still in darkness. One or two traders were opening the shutters of their stalls but there was no-one to see the women as, carrying their baskets and water jars, they slipped by in the shadows, moving quickly towards the

Western gate and out on to the road that led to the place of execution.

The women shivered as they passed that terrible place. Dawn was beginning to break and they could see the dark upright posts that had held the men. Empty now of people the hill still held its memories and its ghosts.

As they approached the garden the pale morning sun rose slowly over the hills and its light gleamed through the gnarled old olive trees that fringed the garden and hid it from the city.

It was easier to pick their way now and the women moved more quickly along the path that twisted between the boulders and the newly planted shrubs.

As the tomb came in view their pace quickened even more and then suddenly Joanna, who was leading the way, stopped in her tracks. 'There's someone already here!' she said 'the stone is rolled back and there's a light inside.'

'Perhaps Joseph or Nicodemus have come' said Mary of Magdala as she eased a jar of water from her shoulder. 'I'm glad they've moved that heavy stone. It's going to make our work much easier.'

Stepping to the mouth of the tomb the women peered in a little nervously not wanting to intrude. It was, after all, Joseph's private tomb. But as they looked they could see no sign of the old man and the light appeared to be coming from the back where Mark and Andrew had placed the body of Jesus.

One by one the women stepped in to the tomb. It was difficult to see clearly but there seemed to be someone sitting on the stone bench. It was a young man and the light surrounded him like a halo.

Startled, the women stood still and the young man spoke 'You have come seeking Jesus of Nazareth' he said 'but see for yourself' and he pointed to a pile of crumpled cloths 'He is not here. He has risen!'

Mary rushed forward to the stone bench. She touched the grave clothes and they flattened to her touch. The women gasped and ran to her side and she turned to the young man 'Where is Jesus?' she cried and her voice filled with panic.

'He is risen!' the young man repeated 'Just as he promised he would.' He smiled at their astonishment. 'Go and tell Simon and the disciples' he said 'tell them quickly. And tell them to go back to Galilee. Jesus will see them there.'

Dropping the spices and the linen the women fled running through the garden to the open space beyond. 'Where do Mark and his mother live?' gasped Mary as they ran.

'I know!' answered Joanna 'It's near the Herodian palace. It's very close!' She ran ahead making for the city walls.

'Stop for a moment!' called Mary beginning to panic 'I can't breathe!'

Joanna stopped running and turned round concerned and Mary collapsed against the wall gasping for breath. 'What's happening?' she cried 'Where's Jesus?' and she began to put her head against the wall in her distress.

The women rushed to her side and Joanna came and gathered her in her arms. 'Mary!' she spoke firmly 'Stop it!' and she rocked her gently until Mary began breathing more evenly and her body relaxed. 'Simon and the others will know what to do' said Joanna calmly.

'They won't!' sobbed Mary and then she looked up sharply 'Who was that young man?'

'I don't know!' admitted Joanna 'Perhaps Joseph left him there to wait for us.'

Mary was not convinced 'Why did he shine like that?' she demanded.

Joanna didn't answer.

'He did shine!' insisted Mary.

'Yes he did!' Joanna agreed 'Can you run now? We should be going.'

'Yes! Yes I can' replied Mary. 'Go on again! We'll follow you!'

The house was still in darkness when they arrived and the city was still quiet. They knocked hurriedly on the door. Mark answered their knocking, a cloth round his body and his eyes bleary with sleep.

He saw the women standing there and, looking at their frightened faces, he pointed to the outside stairs. 'Jesus' friends are up there!' he said 'Go on up!'

Running up the stairs and across the terrace the women rushed to the door of the upper room and pushed it open. The men were still sleeping but the sudden noise jolted many awake. They sat up with eyes wide with bewilderment.

'Jesus has gone!' wailed Mary throwing herself at the lumbering form of Simon. 'The tomb is empty!'

'What!' he grunted staring in surprise at the women.

'The tomb is empty Simon' said Joanna calmly.

'What!' this time it was a roar. 'Who's done this? Who would steal his body?'

The other disciples were on their feet by now wide eyed with horror.

'There was a young man there who said Jesus had risen as he promised us he would' cried Mary.

Simon was pulling on his sandals 'I'm going to see for myself' he shouted and made for the door.

John jumped forward 'Simon' he said firmly 'you don't know where the tomb is. Just wait and I'll show you' and then he too sat down and fastened his sandals while Simon stamped with impatience on the terrace outside. Minutes later they were all running through the streets as John led them to the tomb.

The garden appeared empty but in the new morning light it was possible to see more clearly and, as they turned the corner and the tomb came in sight, they saw a huddled group of soldiers sleeping soundly with a few empty wine skins by their side.

John grinned and turning to the others put his finger to his mouth 'Don't wake them!' he whispered and led the way to the open tomb.

Standing at the entrance John peered in but Simon impatiently pushed him aside and strode inside. There was nothing except the few grave clothes on the far stone bench. With the others blocking the entrance Simon couldn't see into the recesses clearly. 'Get out of the light!' he growled and looked carefully around.

Then he sat down and put his head in his hands. 'Where can he be? Who could have done this terrible thing?'

'Perhaps it's true and Jesus has risen from the dead!' said John eagerly.

Simon gave him a withering look.

'Remember Lazarus' continued John. 'Remember Jairus' little girl and that boy at Nain' John warmed to his theme 'we were there! We saw it happen! Perhaps it's happened here!'

'If that's so' cried Simon 'Where is he?'

John shook his head.

Matthew came forward and grabbed Simon's arm 'You can't do anything here' he said 'We must go back to the room before those soldiers wake!' and pulling Simon to his feet he led him to the opening and the confused and frightened group retraced their steps through the gates and into the city.

Only Mary stayed behind. In her bewilderment and horror she sat on the edge of one of the boulders and gazed at the dark open mouth of the tomb, and she wept.

Suddenly, certain she saw a movement inside the tomb, she ran to the opening and peered in. This time there were two young men sitting there, one at the head and one at the feet, where Jesus' body had lain. 'Why are you weeping?' they asked her.

Mary, determined not to be afraid, said defiantly 'Because they have taken my Lord away and I do not know where they have laid him.'

Just then a movement behind her caused her to turn round quickly and she saw Jesus standing there. His face was in shadow and her eyes were filled with tears so that she did not recognise him. 'Why are you weeping? Who are you looking for?' he asked.

Thinking that this must be the gardener she spoke quickly 'Sir' she said 'Did you move him? Where did you put him? Show me and I will take him away.'

Jesus spoke again 'Mary!' he said and, jolted out of her misery, she looked up in sudden recognition and cried 'Master!' and ran forward in her excitement to fall into his arms.

He stepped back. 'Don't touch me yet Mary!' he said kindly 'I have not yet ascended to my Father. Go to Simon and the others and tell them what you have seen. You have been a faithful, loving friend and I entrust this task to you. Tell them that I am ascending to my Father and your Father. To my God and your God.'

Transfixed with shock Mary began to tremble and she sat down heavily, all the while gazing at her beloved Master. Still gently smiling, as though secretly amused, he slowly disappeared from sight and Mary rubbed her eyes in bewilderment.

'He's alive!' she muttered to herself as confusion was replaced by utter joy. 'He's alive!' and she sprang to her feet and ran towards the city.

'He's alive!' she panted as she swung open the door of the still darkened room. 'He's alive and I've seen him!'

***

It was some time after Mary had left that the soldiers began to wake. It was not yet the first hour of the day but their heads were heavy and their mouths were sour and dry. Grumbling and blaming the cheap wine they staggered to their feet brushing the dust off their uniforms with their hands. It was a moment or two before they saw the stone rolled back from the open mouth of the tomb.

Nobody said a word. As a group they went forward apprehensively to peer inside in the darkness 'It's empty!' said their leader glumly 'Now we're for it!'

'Look!' said another 'Look at all these foot prints!'

'If Pilate hears of this we'll all be punished' their leader was almost in tears 'I'll probably be executed!'

'Well we can't run away and the empty tomb will soon be found' said a seasoned veteran with iron grey hair. 'I suggest we own up to Caiaphas and see if he can help us.'

Caiaphas was in a high temper when the soldiers had told their story. Malchus was despatched to discover the truth and he returned sweating and more than anxious. 'We need a Council meeting immediately!' ordered Caiaphas. 'Get together as many as you can' he ordered the still panting Malchus 'and be quick about it.'

It was not a full Council that gathered but it was a quorum. Caiaphas explained the situation and the gathered men listened gravely. 'This could have far reaching effects' said Annas solemnly.

'I agree!' said Caiaphas 'We must make a decision and we must all agree to stick by it.'

'What are you proposing?' asked a black robed Pharisee.

Caiaphas paused and looked down at his long fingers 'If this man Jesus is thought to have risen from the dead the people will make him a god.'

'Or the Son of God!' interrupted Nicodemus quietly.

'No!' roared the Council in unison rounding on the old man 'Never!'

They turned to Caiaphas 'What then is the solution?' repeated the Pharisee.

'There were new footprints around the mouth of the tomb this morning' said Caiaphas carefully preparing the ground. 'I propose we put the story around that the soldiers were given drugged wine to drink to make them sleep and that during the night the disciples came and stole Jesus' body away in order that his wild exaggerated claims could be seen to be true.'

He looked around 'That could work!' he continued 'And we could bribe the soldiers to stick to that story.'

The Council nodded.

'But we must all agree to stick to the same story' he repeated looking directly at Nicodemus.

'This is the first I have heard of anything' said Nicodemus 'I will decide how to speak when I have discerned the truth.'

Caiaphas groaned with frustration but Annas caught his arm. 'He's old!' he said 'If he starts talking about someone rising from the dead people will say he's soft in the head. Leave him go!'

As the Council members rose to leave Caiaphas turned in fury on Malchus 'Find that body!' he ordered 'It's the only real solution. Without it we're sunk!'

CHAPTER THIRTY SIX

Nicodemus was panting a little as he climbed the stairs outside Mary's house. The morning sun was already hot. 'You must get out of the city!' he gasped as the door to the upper room was opened cautiously. 'Go back to Galilee as quickly as you can!'

The eyes of the disciples widened in alarm.

'Mingle with the other pilgrims or slip out after dark. I don't care how you do it, but do it today!' Once he had regained his composure Nicodemus was brisk and authoritative. 'Caiaphas believes that you have stolen the body of Jesus and is determined to find it. You must get out. Go back to Galilee!'

'Galilee!' repeated Simon stupidly 'That's what Jesus said. He said he's see us in Galilee!'

'When did he say this?' asked Nicodemus sharply.

'Today!' Mary stepped forward. 'I saw him in the garden this morning.'

Nicodemus leaned heavily against the door post 'It's true then?' he whispered.

Mary's face was wreathed in smiles 'It's true!' she exclaimed 'I saw him. I spoke to him. He's alive!'

Nicodemus' old eyes were suddenly filled with tears and he looked around at the now blurred faces of the disciples. 'You must do as he says with out hesitation!' he said 'Nothing must happen to you. You have been witnesses to the most wonderful happening this earth has ever known.' There was wonder in his voice as he spoke, wonder and awe. 'You have a duty to tell the whole world. Why!' he exclaimed 'If Jesus has risen from the dead he has conquered man's ultimate fear!'

Nicodemus looked almost ready to dance with excitement. His eyes shone and he clasped his hands together. But then he paused and took stock. 'Don't leave here together. Go in twos or threes throughout the day. Don't draw attention to yourselves. Stay with the pilgrims.' He looked around 'And make sure you keep this room secret. You might need to use it again and we don't want to get Mary and Mark into trouble.'

He walked over to Simon 'I know Jesus thought well of you. I'm sure you can see that everyone gets safely away.'

Simon looked sheepish 'I let Jesus down' he muttered unhappily. 'I was afraid and I denied even knowing him, not once but three times.'

Nicodemus was solemn 'Then you know what it is like to be afraid and you know what fear can make you do. Don't allow these others to suffer in the same way!' He looked into Simon's eyes 'Remember this experience and use it!' he said 'Make sure all of these good people get out of Jerusalem safely before Caiaphas' men find them.'

A look of determination came into Simon's eyes 'I will!' he said firmly but then he reached out an arm to Nicodemus 'But what has happened to Judas' body? He was one of us too.'

'He's been buried already' said Nicodemus 'In the field where he died' he glared at Simon 'don't you think of going there' he growled 'It will draw attention to you and what good can you do anyway?'

'He was one of us!' repeated Simon stubbornly 'He too made a stupid mistake. But I know you're right. Perhaps we can go there when this is all over.'

'Perhaps!' grunted Nicodemus making for the door. 'Leave it a few months. Caiaphas will have other problems by then!'

***

Caiaphas already did. In an attempt to control the power of his High Priests, Herod the Great had taken to keeping their holy vestments locked up in the Antonia for safe keeping. At special feast occasions he would normally allow them to be released so that they might be worn in public. If the High Priest had offended him the vestments stayed behind lock and key.

Herod was long since dead but Rome's governors had seen this as a remarkably effective way of keeping the High Priests in their place and had continued the practice. The Passover over, the Roman guard had arrived at the Council buildings ready to escort the High Priests to the Antonia with the vestments.

To Caiaphas it mattered not a jot but many of the younger priests found the practice offensive and they were openly defiant. In this they found an ally in the old priest Annas, Caiaphas' father in law.

'It's time to take a stand' said Annas petulantly 'It's demeaning to be dependent upon Pilate like this.'

'Why didn't you take a stand when you were High Priest if you felt so strongly?' Caiaphas was angry 'Why leave it to me!'

Annas didn't even attempt to answer the question 'Pilate's a weak, nasty man' he sneered 'You got the better of him over the matter of the Galilean. You should build on your success. Don't hand over the vestments. Send the soldiers back with a flea in their ear.'

Caiaphas gave a weary shrug and totally ignoring Annas' outburst he clapped his hands and the servants carrying the vestments stepped forward. Then Caiaphas turned to the officer in charge of the guard 'Lets get this business over quickly, I have a lot to do today' and he strode off leaving the disgruntled priests on the steps of the Council building.

'Where's his pride?' complained one of the younger priests 'He allows the Romans to walk all over us just for the sake of peace and quiet.'

Malchus, hovering on the steps behind, interrupted 'You must admit!' he said 'That under Caiaphas things have been peaceful and very, very profitable.'

The young priest turned on Malchus 'Ah the secretary!' they said contemptuously looking him up and down with scorn in their eyes.

'We hear you've lost a body' said one 'how careless!'

***

It took three days for the disciples and those closest to Jesus to get out of Jerusalem and make their way home to Galilee. By the time Simon reached his house the news of what had happened in Jerusalem was already being discussed in hushed voices throughout Capernaum. What had happened at the empty tomb and Jesus' appearance to Mary seemed so far away that the disciples stopped talking about it. Did it really happen? Now they were back in Galilee doubt was already creeping into their hearts. They all returned to their families and began to pick up their lives again but the light had somehow gone out. Without Jesus they felt empty.

Simon's house had always been a home base for the disciples and each day two or three of them would drop by needing to talk and hoping for news. Of them all it was Irena who seemed the most certain of the future. She had always befriended Mary from Magdala and now she spent hours with her, the two women with their heads together talking. It was as though she needed to hear Mary's story every day. And every day it made her more certain 'Be patient!' she'd say to Simon with a smile. 'Jesus is still alive! This is just the beginning!'

'The end more like!' groaned a disheartened Simon when Thomas and Nathaniel dropped round 'This waiting is driving me mad.'

The others nodded as they walked glumly down to the shore to join James and John by the boats. Simon looked at the still lake 'I'm going fishing!' he suddenly decided 'Do you want to come?'

Jolted out of their gloom for a moment they quickly sorted the nets and lit the lamps while John ran back to the house for food. When he returned with a basket brimful of bread and figs and skins of wine the others were ready to push the boat off from the quayside.

'It's the wrong time of the year to catch much' said James.

'It's better than sitting around doing nothing' said Simon and, as a small breeze caught the sail, his face lit up. 'Much better!'

John was right. There was no fish to be found but the six men talked and drank their wine and slept a little. Then they talked some more and the night passed surprisingly quickly.

'It gets light so early these mornings' said Nathaniel watching the fingers of dawn in the east. 'Summer's not far away.'

'We haven't caught anything!' said Thomas.

'It often happens' said Simon with a laugh 'you builders can always count on seeing something for your labours, but we fishermen often labour for no reward at all!'

'My heart bleeds for you!' laughed Thomas. 'It truly does!'

In reply Simon reached down and, scooping up a handful of water, splashed it up into Thomas' laughing face.

Despite the lack of sleep and the disappointment of the catch the trip had done them good. The gloom that had hung over them had lifted.

The little boat was easing around the shore towards Capernaum and the first gleam of the rising sun suddenly bathed them in gold. Shielding his eyes Simon saw a figure on the beach and looking intently his heart lurched. There was something very familiar about the way the stranger was standing. The man called out to them 'Friends, have you caught anything?'

'No!' they chorused.

'Throw out your net on the starboard side. There are fish there!'

Simon's eyes suddenly gleamed with recognition.

'Do it!' he ordered 'Do it quickly!'

Andrew grabbed hold of the net and spun it over his head. As it landed in the water and began to sink everyone could see at once the fish captured in the perfect circle.

John looked at Simon in amazement and seeing the happiness in Simon's eyes he looked at the man on the beach 'It's the Lord' he cried 'It's Jesus!'

'Yes!' Simon agreed happily. 'It is!' and pulling his clothes around him he climbed quickly on to the gunwale and jumped into the sea. The water was deeper than he had thought and as he struggled to wade in Jesus stepped in to the water and gave him a hand.

'Simon!' laughed Jesus as they climbed together on to the shore 'Aren't you ever going to learn how to swim?'

'Oh my dear Lord!' wept Simon 'You were right. I was so weak and I denied you three times.'

'I know!' agreed Jesus tenderly 'You were afraid!'

'But you needed me' Simon continued to weep.

Jesus held him at arm's length 'It is your love I need' he said 'do you love me?'

'Yes Lord' replied Simon wiping his eyes roughly 'you know that I love you.'

Jesus looked into Simon's eyes 'You remember' he said 'when I talked about loving the people as a shepherd loves his sheep?' Simon nodded 'I am the Good Shepherd' continued Jesus 'and I will lead God's people to his love and you' he caught hold of Simon's hands as he spoke 'you will help me. You will feed my lambs.'

'I might let you down again' said Simon glumly.

Jesus smiled 'I don't think you will' he said 'but the others are coming with the fish. Let's have some breakfast and then we'll talk some more!'

With the boat gently bobbing on the clear water of the lake and the sun tingeing all with gold the disciples gazed at Jesus in wonder. Andrew had to pinch himself to make sure he was not dreaming. 'When John and I carried you into Joseph's tomb' he said with a worried frown 'we were sure you were dead!'

'Are you a ghost?' asked John anxiously.

'Come and touch me and see for yourself' replied Jesus stretching out a hand.

As he did so John saw for the first time the wound on Jesus' wrist and he stepped back horrified.

'No John!' said Jesus 'Touch my hand. I want you to be sure of what you see.' He looked at the others 'you too Thomas, and all of you. You cannot go out and do my work if you have doubt in your hearts.'

Gingerly each of the men stepped forward and touched Jesus' hand. When Thomas saw the ragged wound he fell to his knees 'My Lord and my God' he exclaimed and Jesus looked down at him with great compassion. 'Because you have seen for yourself your doubts are vanquished' he said 'but I am sending you all out to those who will never be able to see for themselves, but because of you and your belief they too will believe and will be blessed.'

Too frightened to speak they stood in silence gazing at their beloved master. How had this happened? Was it possible they were dreaming?

Then Jesus chuckled 'The fish smells good. Let's go and eat' and he led the way to a charcoal fire and began to pick the lightly crisped fish from the grill handing pieces to then all. He began then to tear off pieces of white succulent fish and put them in his mouth and he looked at John 'Ghosts don't eat fish' he said with a grin 'they don't have bodies like this that need food' and he slapped his hand against his thigh. 'But I'm glad I do!' he continued happily 'This is really delicious!'

Then he drew Simon aside and they walked a little way up towards the trees. 'Simon, Son of Jonah, do you love me?' asked Jesus forcing Simon to look into his eyes.

'Yes Lord!' replied Simon 'You know that I love you!'

'Simon, Son of Jonah,' asked Jesus again 'do you really love me?'

Simon was hurt. 'Lord' he said 'you know everything. You know that I love you. Why do you need to ask me three times?' and then suddenly his face crumpled 'Three times' he repeated 'you've asked me three times because I denied you three times!'

'Yes Simon!' agreed Jesus with a smile 'And now with your love you have wiped those denials from the slate and you are free of guilt.'

Jesus watched as Simon visibly relaxed and his anxious frown uncreased and then he took his friend by the arm and said 'Do you remember once when I nicknamed you Peter the Rock?'

'Of course!' agreed Simon eagerly. 'In Caesarea Philippi.'

'I want you to be Simon the Rock from now onwards. I want you to feed my sheep and lead them to God and I want you to feed them with love. Show them that even when they fail the love of God never fails.'

Simon nodded 'Thank you!' he whispered.

'Come now Simon Peter!' said Jesus with a smile 'I am going now but I want you to gather all the disciples and take them to our mountain. Take the boat home first and then go and collect the others. I will be waiting for you!'

'Of course' agreed Simon Peter and walking ahead of Jesus towards the shore he called to Andrew. 'Pull the boat in Andrew. We've got to get the others.'

'Where's Jesus?' asked John looking towards the trees. Simon Peter swung round. Jesus was nowhere in sight.

It was late in the day by the time all the disciples had been found and Simon Peter was beginning to fret, but as they climbed the hill where Jesus had done so much of his teaching in the past, Jesus could be seen clearly waiting, sitting on a boulder ahead of them.

They gathered around him in excitement and he spoke to each one and allowed them to touch him and didn't object when they just gaped, open mouthed. Finally he suggested that they sat down so that he could speak and as the excited conversation died away he began to talk to them all.

'The time has come' he said 'for me to leave you. You will not see me in person again but I will always be with you in spirit.'

The disciples nodded, remembering when he had sent them out in twos how they had felt him working by their side, never leaving them.

'I give to you all' Jesus continued 'the authority to preach and heal in my name, to tell the world of God's love and to use this love as a force against evil. I want you to baptise people in my name and as I chose you to be my disciples so I want you to go out and make disciples of all nations.'

As the enormity of what Jesus was saying began to sink in so did the fear. 'Never fear!' said Jesus 'I will be with you always, even to the end of time' and he stood up so that they had to look up to see his face.

'I want you to go back to Jerusalem' he said 'go back and travel with the pilgrims going to the feast of Pentecost. That way you won't be noticed. When you get to the city find your way to Mary's house once more and wait. Wait and you will receive the power you need to carry out your work.'

'Power?' demanded Andrew 'Like yours you mean?'

'Yes Andrew!' replied Jesus 'Power from on high. The power of love!'

Andrew's face showed his fear. 'We've seen what it can do' he whispered 'we've seen how it consumes your life. How are we able to receive this power?'

'Just remember Andrew' said Jesus kindly 'It is the power of God's love. It is compassionate and true. It will never hurt you. It will be a blessing.'

Andrew looked doubtful 'Where are you going?' he asked.

'I am going' said Jesus 'to prepare a place for you all in my Father's house and when the time is right I shall come for you and take you to me.'

Thomas was anxious 'How will we know the way?'

Jesus smiled 'I am the way, the truth and the life. Stay with me and I will lead you.'

Jesus took a step on to the boulder he had been sitting on and looked above their heads to the sea and the hills beyond. 'I am going to my Father and you should be glad for me.' He looked down at them all 'I will always be by your side in spirit and anything you ask in my name I will do. Never fear' he continued 'power will come to you from on high. I would not leave you comfortless.'

And he lifted his hands 'Peace!' he said 'That is my parting gift to you. My peace I give to you, not as the world gives it, but the peace of God which passes all understanding. May peace be with you all.'

And as he spoke a mist came down from the lake and wreathed its way among them all. When it cleared Jesus had disappeared.

CHAPTER THIRTY SEVEN

'If you're all going up to Jerusalem again for Pentecost I'm going to!' declared Irena stubbornly, daring the family to oppose her.

Sarah, startled, turned to her mother 'It's a long journey' she said anxiously 'do you think you are up to it!'

'I'm not in my dotage yet!' snapped Irena 'And I've never felt better. Besides which' she said wistfully 'Jesus said something would happen and I want to be there!'

'Don't worry Sarah' smiled Simon 'if we leave a day early and pace ourselves she should manage very well.'

'Mary of Magdala also wants to come and so does Jesus' mother' said Andrew.

'My mother too' added John 'and Joanna.' He looked at Irena 'So you'll have plenty of company.'

Irena scowled at the two young men 'I know what's going through your heads!' she grumbled 'You're thinking that if we all come we'll do the cooking!'

John grinned 'Well won't you?' he asked and Irena laughed and then looked up at Simon enquiringly.

Returning her look Simon smiled and nodded 'You were very precious to Jesus' he said 'you should come!'

The journey was far easier than Irena had expected. The weather was hot and they rested at midday, walking only in the morning and starting again in the late afternoon. It was decided that the women should stay with Lazarus and his sisters but, because Malchus lived in Bethany, it would be better if the disciples were to go again to Mary and Mark's house and lie low.

The city was beginning to fill up again for the first harvest festival of the year. The weather had been kind and the farmers were grateful, so there were many peasant families wanting to give thanks.

The feast of Pentecost was always fifty days after Passover and did not command such large numbers of pilgrims, but it was a joyous feast and the Romans didn't bother to put on extra troops. There was never any trouble at Pentecost.

Also at Pentecost the religious Jews had begun to give thanks to God for the laws and commandments that had been passed down to them through Moses. The scribes and the Pharisees were much in evidence and seemed determined that one day they would take over this peasant festival and give it a more serious meaning.

Watching from the Upper Room as groups of the black robed scholars walked down the road on their way to the Temple, Matthew screwed his face up in distaste. 'It is on occasions like this that I really miss Judas' pithy comments' he said.

Simon looked up sharply 'I want to find where Judas is buried' he said 'will you come with me tonight Matthew? We could go when it gets dark.'

Matthew was pleased to be asked 'Yes' he agreed 'you all know that Jesus asked me to keep an eye on Judas when he first joined us' he said and everyone nodded sadly. 'Well!' he continued 'I grew to like him. He was passionate and young but he had a good heart.'

'He just made a silly mistake in trusting someone like Malchus' said Simon 'but when you're young you want to trust people. It's only as you grow older that you learn to be cautious and suspicious.'

'If I give you a small stone will you take it for me?' asked Nathaniel.

'Of course!' agreed Simon.

'And one from me!' chorused John and Andrew.

Simon laughed 'We'll take stones from everyone as long as they are small enough.'

That night after dark the two men made their way quietly through the streets down to the Kidron Valley. They knew whereabouts the place was but were anxious about finding it in the dark. They needn't have worried. It was a clear summer night and the sky was alive with stars. A mound of white washed stones stood alone in the middle of a small field. A sturdy thorn tree grew out of the broken wall that surrounded it.

The loneliness of this young man's grave was enough to bring Simon and Matthew to their knees. 'O Lord be with him!' whispered Matthew.

'Forgive him Lord' Simon prayed and he turned to Matthew 'It could so easily have been me!' he groaned.

Searching in their small leather bags hanging from their waists the two men solemnly took out the pebbles the others had given them and placed them on the white mound and, as they did so, they named each disciple in turn.

When they returned to the others Peter was thoughtful 'We need to appoint someone to take Judas' place' he said 'someone who has been with us from the beginning, someone who has faithfully followed Jesus and who has heard his words.' He looked at them all 'Who do you suggest?'

There were two obvious candidates, Justus and Matthias. Each had been a faithful and enthusiastic disciple. Simon took a jar with a narrow neck and selecting two small pebbles he marked each, one with a J and the other M, and then he dropped the pebbles into the jar and got to his feet.

Lifting the jar high he said firmly 'You choose Lord!' and he shook the jar violently until one of the pebbles flew out through the narrow neck.

It fell on the floor and Matthew picked it up and held it to the light 'It's M!' he said 'Matthias.'

The next day James came looking for them. He had visited Mary in Bethany and Lazarus had directed him to their hiding place. 'Here you all are!' he grinned as he opened the door and found the young men 'What Malchus wouldn't give for a sight like this!'

'Is he still looking for us?' asked Philip anxiously.

'Not so urgently!' admitted James. 'The first two weeks after you left he seemed to be going mad. He had the soldiers out everywhere. He turned the city upside down!' James smiled at the memory 'He needed to find Jesus' body so he could disprove your story. He's sure you've hidden it somewhere.'

The disciples were surprised 'How would that have been possible?' they asked, alarm appearing in their eyes.

'We were all separated' said Matthew 'and scared!'

'We'd run away!' agreed John sadly.

'Didn't Caiaphas put a guard around the tomb?' asked Nathaniel.

'Yes he did!' said James 'And it's the soldiers that have been spreading the story. They say you gave them drugged wine to drink and while they were asleep you came and stole the body and hid it so that you could tell the world that Jesus has risen from the dead!'

'He has risen!' said Simon quietly and James' eyes opened wide. 'We've all seen him and he told us to be here in this room for the feast of Pentecost!'

James was quiet 'I'd heard the rumours' he said 'but I thought it was wishful thinking.' His face grew solemn 'Each one of you has seen him? There is no mistake?'

'No James. There is no mistake,' said Simon 'your brother has defeated the power of death.'

James sat down heavily 'I'm not disputing what you say' he said 'but Jesus was my brother. We grew up together. He was a wonderful brother but it never occurred to me that he was different from everyone else.' He paused 'At least not until he started his mission and the miracles started happening' he said as he put his head in his hands 'It's a lot to take in!'

John sat beside him and put an arm over James' shoulders 'He came to us just as he said he would' he said. 'He was real. We touched him and he told us to come here. We wouldn't lie to you!'

'No!' said James 'I know you wouldn't.'

***

The Sabbath began at sundown and the young men shared their Sabbath meal together. The memory of their last meal in this place lay heavily on them all and one by one they went quietly to their bed rolls and dropped asleep.

The following morning they were woken by the noisy pilgrims as they came into the city through the Western Gate. The sun was already hot and strong and they could see the rays piercing the edges of the shutters.

A gentle knock on the door revealed the group of women with Lazarus and his sisters. Irena bustled into the room carrying a heavy basket. 'Come on you boys' she ordered 'stow your beds away and get out the table! We've brought you some hot rolls and some goat cheese.' She gave Andrew a none-to-gentle thump with her foot as she hurried past his recumbent form. 'Get up Andrew!' she said happily 'It's a beautiful day and it's years since I was in the city. I don't want to waste a moment!'

'Do you have to be so cheerful' groaned Andrew as he struggled to his feet 'It's still the middle of the night!'

'It's the second hour already!' Irena retorted 'The city is filling up.' She began to put the food on the table and the women came to help her. 'Eat!' she ordered.

With a mouthful of steaming bread Andrew continued to grumble 'We can't go into the city. Caiaphas' men are still looking for us. We must stay in hiding.'

'James found us yesterday' added Simon 'and told us the hunt is still on. It's dangerous to go out.'

'I think I'll go back to bed!' Andrew made for his bed roll but Joanna got there first and rolled it neatly away.

Simon smiled but said solemnly 'Even if we must stay here we should wash and tidy ourselves up.' He paused and looked at them all 'We should be ready!'

Nobody asked him what they had to be ready for. Without further questions they tidied up the room and when Mary and Joanna had fetched water they all washed and prepared themselves for whatever the day had to offer.

Sitting on the cushions around the table they began to reminisce 'Do you remember when those men let the paralytic down through the roof?' asked Andrew laughing 'I thought Irena would have a heart attack!'

'And the look on the scribes' faces when Jesus put them right about the Sabbath!' exclaimed Philip.

'He never seemed afraid of anyone' said Simon.

'And he was fun to be with' John said glumly.

A silence filled the room and then Mary of Magdala, speaking for them all, said 'I really miss him!' and they all nodded unhappily. Suddenly without warning, the door flew open. Looking up in alarm they watched as it banged back against the wall, violently wrenching the hinges from the post. Then the shutters on the windows shattered into little pieces and with a deep roar a fierce wind drove into the room. It whirled and whipped around the disciples and as each of them gasped for breath they felt as though they were swallowing fire. Jumping to their feet in panic as the fire raced through their bodies they staggered and swayed in the force of the wind. Then as suddenly as it had come, the wind died down and they stood and looked at each other in amazement.

The door still hung limply on its broken hinges but the air was still once more, and quiet.

'What has happened?' cried Mary.

'I feel as if I could take on the world' exclaimed Simon excitedly.

'He's come as he said he would' said John with wonder in his eyes. 'His spirit is with us!'

'I don't feel afraid anymore!' said Nathaniel.

'Nor I' agreed Philip.

'Jesus is here!' cried Mary of Magdala. 'I feel him present' she caught her hands to her breast 'here in my heart!'

'He said he would send a Comforter' said James 'but what he's sent is his own spirit.' He looked thoughtful 'That's why he had to die' he continued 'so that he could release his spirit into the world.'

Irena put her arm around Mary 'He always said that if we thought of him with love he would be there' she smiled at the younger woman. 'When you told us how much you missed him it was obvious how much you loved him. And he came as he said he would.'

Simon strode to the door 'What are we doing hiding in here?' he exclaimed 'It doesn't matter if Malchus can find us. We have a message of love to tell and if God wants us to tell it nothing or no-one will stop us.'

The others scrambled eagerly to their feet and followed him out on to the roof top. Below them in the street pilgrims pushed and shoved their way down towards the Temple. Through the Western Gate especially pilgrims of all nationalities could be seen and the disciples looked down on a sea of colour.

Following Simon they leaned on the parapet and with Simon leading the way they began to call down to the crowd and tell them about Jesus. It was disorganised and each was telling his own story but the crowd below stopped moving and looked up surprised. Then they stood still and began to listen.

As they spoke the people in the crowd were mystified 'What language are they speaking?' they asked. 'How is it that we can all understand what they are saying?'

'Who is this Jesus they are talking about?' asked someone.

'He's the Messiah!' said another 'And they are saying that God has raised him from the dead.'

'Take no notice!' said a rougher voice 'You're blocking the street. Why are you bothering with these men? It's obvious that they are drunk!'

'Drunk!' roared Simon Peter raising himself to his full height 'Why it's not yet the third hour!' he said indignantly. 'Listen to me!' he demanded and the crowds were quiet.

'We are all Jews' he said 'We have all been waiting for God to send us a Messiah. And we believe we will know the Messiah when he comes because there will be signs and wonders done in his name.'

'The man Jesus, from Nazareth, was our Master. Through him many people were healed and wondrous signs were seen. He was truly the Messiah. But we Jews have killed our own Messiah by allowing the Romans to crucify him.'

'But God has raised him from the dead and we, his followers, have all seen him and spoken to him and today, here and now he has sent his spirit among us to give us the courage to stand here and talk to you all.'

'God has fulfilled his promise.' Simon Peter paused 'And you are the first to hear the Good News!'

The crowd began to mutter 'If we killed the Messiah we're all doomed' shouted a man looking up at the disciples.

'What can we do?' called out another.

Peter looked down and his heart was filled with sorrow for the people 'You can be baptised in the name of Jesus to wash away the guilt and you can start your lives again, free from sin.'

He looked around. Further down the street was a synagogue with a mikveh at its entrance. Simon Peter made for the stairs 'Those of you who want to be baptised follow me!' he called and, bounding down the steps, he made for the synagogue.

'Take off your outer cloaks and step forward' he said eagerly. Mesmerised by his confidence and the force of his argument the crowd pushed forward. One by one they stepped down into the cleansing waters of the mikveh. Dressed only in their white under shifts they climbed down the narrow steps.

Simon Peter put his hand on each head and pushed it briefly below the clean water. 'I baptise you in the name of Jesus the Messiah' he said, and the other disciples stepped forward to lead the new convert away.

Over three thousand people became believers that first day, and when the news reached Malchus his heart sank.

CHAPTER THIRTY EIGHT

It took all morning for the excited pilgrims to clear and to drift off down the street to the Temple. As the last two walked away the disciples moved forward and gathered together around the mikveh. Eyes alight with amazement and joy they hugged each other happily.

'He said he would always be with us' exclaimed John 'and he is! I can feel him!'

'I've never felt so alive1' said Thomas grinning from ear to ear.

Andrew jumped on to the edge of the mikveh 'I'm not going to spend my time skulking around in shadows anymore' he said firmly 'what can Caiaphas do anyway?'

'Nothing of any importance' agreed Simon 'that's for certain!'

'Death is really only the beginning of something new isn't it?' mused John.

'Something new, and glorious and exciting!' Simon's voice rose as his realisation grew.

A figure stepped out from the shadows of the doorway across the street and Simon swung round quickly. James stepped forward into the midst of them all 'I didn't mean to startle anyone' he said 'but I've been watching you for some time.' He paused 'I came back to talk to you and found that you have already started to change the world!'

The disciples laughed, but Simon looked at Jesus' brother enquiringly 'What is it you wanted to talk about?' he asked.

James hesitated and looked around at them all 'I haven't seen Jesus since we laid him in Joseph's tomb' he said 'but you all tell me that you have seen him alive.'

'Yes, we have!' exclaimed John 'It's true!'

James smiled and nodded. 'I'm envious!' he admitted 'I wish I had seen him too!' He hesitated again 'But I've been turning it over and over in my mind and I've come to tell you all that I believe you.'

The disciples exchanged delighted glances.

'All the time we were growing up' continued James 'there was never a time when Jesus lied to me or even exaggerated something in order to please me. He was always straight forward and truthful.'

'I could trust him,' James smiled 'and if he says there is a life after death, and if he has died in order that we need never be afraid again then why should I not believe him now?'

'I believe him and I believe you all' he said gravely and he took off his coat and folded it on the wall. 'Simon will you baptise me? I want so much to show you all how much I trust you and above all I want my brother to stay with me. I love him too much to allow us to be separated by anything as inconsequential as death!'

A delighted Simon reached out a hand and grasping James' arm led him to the steps of the mikveh. With great dignity James proudly stepped down into the cold water, his white shift swirling around him as he descended.

'I baptise you in the name of Jesus the Messiah' said Simon as he put his hand on James' head and pushed him under the water.

When he surfaced again James stood still and allowed the water to run down his face and he looked gravely around. 'I'm not an excitable sort of person as you well know!' he said slowly 'But I feel at peace. This was something I had to do!'

Simon reached down to help him up the steps 'you always were steady and serious' he agreed 'and far too clever for all of us!'

The disciples nodded, grinning their agreement. 'We're just country bumpkins' continued Simon 'and we're useless in these sophisticated places.' He put his arm around James' wet shoulders 'We're going to need your help and advice if you are willing.'

James looked at him with a smile in his eyes 'Of course I will help' he said 'but you will manage well enough even without me. To be honest' he continued 'if I had any reason to doubt in the wonderful stories you have to tell, just witnessing the change in all of you would be enough to convince me a hundred times over!'

The disciples looked at each other bemused and James laughed 'Look at you all!' he exclaimed 'Only a few hours ago you were frightened peasants lost in the big city. Now you are full of confidence and are ready to take on the world. Anyone just looking at you cannot help but believe!'

Simon stood tall 'The day is slipping away' he said 'let's go to the Temple and give God the thanks he deserves.'

Ignoring the water still dripping from his clothes James picked up his cloak and joined the group as they clattered happily down the cobbled street.

The street widened out at the junction with another wider road which led further down to the pool of Siloam. Ahead of them, across this road, stood the majestic stairways and arches that led beneath the Council buildings of the Temple and up into the courts themselves.

They eagerly climbed the steps to the towering gate way in the wall. Its huge doors were open and inviting, and the carved plants and flowers gilded with gold and silver, which adorned the gate posts, were clearly visible. This was the Gate Beautiful, a tribute to the demented genius of Herod the Great, whose vision had made this whole building come to life.

Sitting in the afternoon sun there was a beggar leaning against one of the pillars. Seeing the disciples approach he leaned forward anxiously with arms outstretched 'Spare me some coins!' he pleaded 'I am crippled and in great need.'

Both Simon and John stepped towards him eager to help and the man's eyes flashed with anticipation. Then Simon said 'Look at us!' and the man looked up expectantly.

Simon looked at him and said 'I have no silver or gold, but what I have I give to you!' and he reached down and took the man's outstretched hand.

'In the name of Jesus Christ of Nazareth stand up and walk!' he said and pulled the man gently to his feet.

As he did so the man's ankles and feet became strong and, shaking himself free of Simon's hand, he leapt to his feet and began jumping and running for joy. He made for the temple courts loudly praising God for his cure and the disciples followed behind laughing to see his joy.

Inside the courts the stall holders, all local men, were astounded. The cripple was well known to them all and they gathered around, utterly astonished. Simon, seizing the opportunity, jumped on to a wall and called for silence. 'How is it that you, men of Israel, can wonder at such things?' he challenged them.

'This man is able to walk again because of Jesus of Nazareth, a man sent to you by God himself. But you!' he shouted, pointing at them all, 'You rejected him and had him killed.'

The disciples moved in closer to Simon's side. 'But this Jesus has risen from the dead and we are all witnesses' continued Simon 'we have seen him and it is in his name, not ours, that this man has been cured.'

'If this is true' shouted one of the stall holders 'what can we do?'

'Repent!' demanded Simon 'Look again at your lives and turn them around. Turn to God that your sins may be wiped out!'

The crowds pushed inwards as people craned their necks to see what was going on and the disciples clambered up next to Simon to prevent being trampled. From this vantage point they could see the temple officials and the priests as, led by Malchus, they hurried to the scene. The crowd parted to let them through and in the hush that followed Malchus smartly ordered the guards to arrest all the perpetrators of this riot. All the disciples were rounded up. Even the cripple was arrested and with obvious satisfaction Malchus followed the prisoners out of the court to the rooms below the Council Hall.

With the disciples safely locked away Malchus hurried to Caiaphas 'We've got them!' he said triumphantly 'All of them!'

'At last!' sighed Caiaphas 'Question them! Find out everything about them. I want an end to all this nonsense. We have a council meeting and if necessary we'll have the whole lot of them executed as agitators.'

'I think not' sneered the grating voice of old Annas as he came hurriedly into the room. 'Haven't you heard?' he continued 'They've healed someone in the name of the Jesus and now the whole of the city is in turmoil.'

Caiaphas sat down heavily 'Will there be no end to all of this' he groaned.

'Some of the city people are planning on holding an all night vigil at the Gate Beautiful' Annas smiled maliciously 'you'll not be able to do anything to these men if the city is on their side.'

Caiaphas looked at his father in law's smug face 'We'll see in the morning!' he snarled, and turning to Malchus 'Make sure every single one of the Council attends' he said.

The following morning the whole Council was in attendance and the prisoners were brought before them. If they had expected men cowed by the predicament they found themselves in they were to be disappointed. Why, some of them even looked as if they were enjoying the whole business.

One-by-one they questioned the disciples 'Who was this man Jesus and where was his body?' they demanded The disciples responded eagerly and boldly told their excited story. Their conviction startled the

Council members and when they heard the testimony of the cripple they realised that they had an even greater problem then they first thought.

Ordering the prisoners out of the room Caiaphas looked around at the Council 'What shall we do?' he asked. 'The people of the city are all clamouring for their release, but if we let them go to continue this charade it will all get completely out of hand.'

'Get the leader back in. That man Simon' said Annas 'and warn him! Threaten him! Frighten him! Do whatever it takes to make him stop! He's only an ignorant fisherman. Put the fear of God into him.'

'Bring him back' growled Caiaphas to Malchus.

When Simon stood once more before the Council Caiaphas warned him 'We order you not to teach the people about his man Jesus. You are not to speak of him at all. If you disobey us we will arrest you again and have you stoned to death.'

Simon paled but stood defiantly silent.

Caiaphas smiled. He knew his message had gone home. 'Disobey us and you'll never see your wife or son again' he warned.

Simon looked up in alarm. How did the High Priest know of his family? He glanced towards the grimly smiling Malchus and then took a deep breath and steadied himself. 'Whether it is right in God's sight to listen to you rather than God, you must judge' he said. 'For my part I cannot keep from speaking about what we have seen and heard.'

'My companions and I' continued Simon 'have been witnesses to the most amazing things. Our leader and friend Jesus of Nazareth, whom you killed' Simon paused accusingly 'has been exalted to God's right hand and has given his Holy Spirit to all who obey him.'

'In the strength of this Spirit' Simon said firmly 'I can do nothing but proclaim that Jesus is the Messiah, the very Son of God.'

Council members jumped to their feet and began to shout and Caiaphas took a while to calm them down. Ordering Simon from the room Caiaphas waited until he had left and then said 'What do you think? Shall we have him stoned?'

Some of the Council members jumped again to their feet and shouted 'Death! Death to the fisherman!' And then an elderly man got to his feet and walked into the middle of the floor where the prisoners had stood. He stood there in silence and gradually the Council members sat down.

Gamaliel was the most respected of all the rabbis in the country. He was a wise, compassionate man. He waited patiently for his fellow Council members to be silent and then he spoke 'Fellow Israelites, consider carefully what you propose to do with these men. There have been Messiahs before but they have all come to nothing. I suggest you leave these men well alone. Time will resolve our problem. If it is not of God it will die,' he paused and his expression challenged them all 'but if it is of God, who can stand against it?'

He looked around at them all and his eyes rested on Caiaphas 'Why' he said sternly 'you may even be found to be fighting against God!'

In the silence that ensued the Council members turned as a man to watch Caiaphas. How would he respond?

Caiaphas pulled himself slowly to his feet. His back ached 'I must be getting old' he thought suddenly and then, scowling down at Malchus, he said 'have them flogged. Warn them again and then release them!' he glared around. 'Time will tell if any of this is true' he said and his voice was tired 'but I don't suppose any of us will live long enough to find out!'

Looking down at Malchus again he sighed 'Don't ever stop looking for that body!' he ordered. 'If you don't find it, that accursed man will have turned our world upside down.' There was a tremor in his voice when he spoke again. Spreading wide his arms he addressed the assembled Council 'All we represent; this Temple and all its splendour; the glory of this ancient city; our traditions, our heritage,' he paused again as he drew a deep breath. 'It will all count for nothing!'